THE ELECTRICAL ALARM CONTRACTOR EXAM WORKBOOK

This book is written to help prepare an electrician for the state electrical alarm examination.

The correct installation of an alarm system is very critical when lives and property are being protected.

Many states are now requiring electricians to be tested and licensed prior to installing alarm systems. Alarm installations must conform to the applicable National Electrical Code® (NEC®) which is the minimum requirements permitted. Local codes can be more stringent than the NEC®.

The difference between general wiring and alarm wiring is open circuits are supervised. This book will explain the different types of circuits such as open loop, closed loop, Class 1, Class 2, Class 3, power-limited, nonpower-limited, remote-control, fire protective signaling systems, supervised circuits, non-supervised circuits, etc.

This workbook will cover the questions from the alarm exam from the National Electrical Code®, OSHA, UL, NFPA, Business Law, etc. with a final exam from each section. This exam workbook will help you become more familiar with the NEC, OSHA, UL, NFPA and Business law. Knowing where to find the answer to an exam question within the allowed time is the key to passing the exam.

While every precaution has been taken in the preparation of this book, the author and publisher assumes no responsibility for errors or omissions. Neither is any liability assumed from the use of the information contained herein.

National Electrical Code® and NEC® are Registered Trademarks of the National Fire Protection Association, Inc., Quincy, MA.

9th Printing   ISBN 978-0-945495-41-3

HENRY PUBLICATIONS SINCE 1985

STATE ELECTRICAL ALARM CONTRACTOR EXAMINATION BLUEPRINT 7 1/2 HOUR EXAM

The examination is 2 parts, the technical/safety part is 100 questions open book with a 5 hour time limit. The business part is 50 questions open book with a 21/2 hour time limit.

BUSINESS EXAM 50 QUESTIONS (COMPUTER EXAM)

UNEMPLOYMENT COMPENSATION
WORKERS' COMPENSATION
CIRCULAR E
CHAPTERS 489, 61G6 and 633
ACCOUNTING
AMERICANS WITH DISABILITY ACT
BONDING, CONTRACTING and SUBCONTRACTING
HANDY REFERENCE GUIDE TO FAIR LABOR
CONSTRUCTION LIEN LAW
RECORD KEEPING GUIDELINES for OCCUPATIONAL INJURIES

PART II   TECHNICAL/SAFETY PART (COMPUTER EXAM)

GENERAL THEORY and ELECTRICAL PRINCIPLES
PLAN, SCHEMATICS and DIAGRAM READING and INTERPRETATION
WIRING and PROTECTION
WIRING METHODS and MATERIALS
SPECIAL OCCUPANCIES and SITUATIONS
OSHA, SAFETY, PROCEDURES FOR TESTING AND USE OF TOOLS and EQUIPMENT
AMERICANS WITH DISABILITIES ACT
LIMITED ENERGY/LOW VOLTAGE
CENTRAL STATION FACILITIES and SIGNALING
PREMISES PROTECTIVE SIGNALING SYSTEMS
INITIATING DEVICES
BURGLAR ALARMS

REQUIRED
REFERENCE BOOKs

STATE UNEMPLOYMENT COMPENSATION LAW

WORKERS' COMPENSATION LAW

FIRE MARSHAL CODE

LICENSING LAWS 489 PART II AND 61 G6

EMPLOYERS' TAX GUIDE, CIRCULAR E

OVERTIME COMPENSATION FAIR LABOR STANDARDS LAW

OSHA SAFETY and HEALTH STANDARDS

ACCOUNTING

AMERICANS WITH DISABILITY ACTS

BONDING, CONTRACTING AND SUBC0NTRACTING

RECORD KEEPING GUIDELINES

NATIONAL ELECTRICAL CODE

NFPA #72 - NATIONAL FIRE ALARM CODE

NFPA #101 LIFE SAFETY CODE

UL - 365 POLICE STATION CONNECTED
BURGLAR ALARM UNITS AND SYSTEMS

UL - 681 INSTALLATION and CLASSIFICATION of
MERCANTILE and
BANK BURGLAR ALARM SYSTEMS

FIRE ALARM SIGNALING SYSTEMS HANDBOOK

UNDERSTANDING AND SERVICING ALARM SYSTEMS

SECURITY, A GUIDE TO SECURITY SYSTEM DESIGN

TELECOMMUNICATION WIRING

The listed references can be purchased by ☎ **1-800-642-2633**
http://www.code-electrical.com

CONTENTS

INSTALLATION of WIRING

The primary rule is: "Follow the manufacturer's instructions."

The requirement for electrical supervision of the installation wires and their connections to initiating devices and appliances makes fire alarm system wiring very different from general wiring.

Any variance from the manufacturer's drawings might cause a portion of a circuit to be unsupervised and, if an open or short occurred, prevent the circuit from performing its intended function, and possibly lead to loss of life.

The rules are complex and it requires an installer that is a specialist in fire alarm system installations.

Since there are at least a dozen accepted exceptions to wire installation supervision, and not all may apply to every job, the alarm installer **must "Follow the manufacturer's instructions."**

Installers of alarm systems using typical drawings should be well qualified in fire alarm system installation requirements or be under the **direct** supervision of someone who is well qualified.

Opens account for the largest percentage of circuit problems. Opens can result from bad splices, cut wires, loose connections, bad solder joints, etc. The most dangerous fault is a **foreign potential** on the circuit. Someone not knowing what they are doing connecting the alarm circuit to a 120 volt branch circuit wire or other equipment. Short circuits can result from sharp objects such as duct systems cutting the wire, staples driven too tight, etc. Grounds can occur from dirt or moisture.

Care must be taken in this installation of an alarm system.

What makes a fire alarm circuit different from any other electrical circuit is that an **open** in most circuits simply prevents some of the circuit components from working; while an **open** in a fire alarm circuit also causes the fire alarm panel to indicate trouble whenever the system is not 100% operable.

Never loop an unbroken wire around a fire alarm device terminal. **Always** cut or break the circuit wires before connecting them to a fire alarm device. The reason is if a vandal disconnects the looped wire, or if the screw breaks or loosens the device would be disabled, but supervisory current will continue flowing through the looped wire. So the fire alarm panel **won't** indicate trouble - even though part of the system can't work.

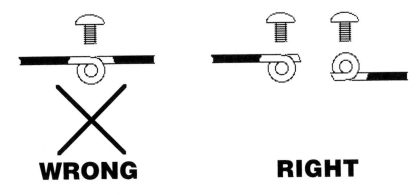

WRONG   **RIGHT**

Wiring connections to the device **cannot** be "T" tapped. The control panel checks the condition of the wiring by constantly running a small amount of current from the panel, through the end-of-line device, and back into the panel. If you "T" tap this **supervisory current**, the supervisory current won't run through the "T" tapped leg. An open on that leg won't show up at the panel. You need to "Y" tap the device as shown in the diagram below.

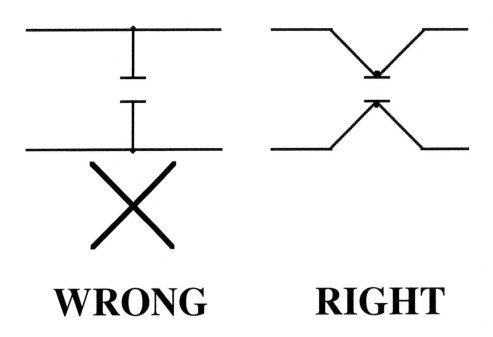

WRONG   RIGHT

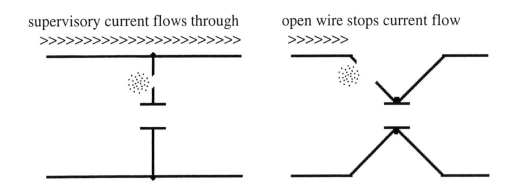

supervisory current flows through
>>>>>>>>>>>>>>>>>>>>>>>>>>

open wire stops current flow
>>>>>>>>

Smoke detectors are a two-part units, they consist of a base and a head. The base connects to the circuit wiring and mounts on a back box; the head is a removable unit which fits on the base. Since a smoke detector head can be removed, it is possible for a vandal to remove a smoke detector without disturbing the smoke detector base or the circuit wiring.

Smoke detector manufacturers design their bases so that the **removal** of the smoke detector will cause the control panel to see an **open** circuit condition. The diagram below shows the head **missing**, so an open exists between 1+ and 2+.

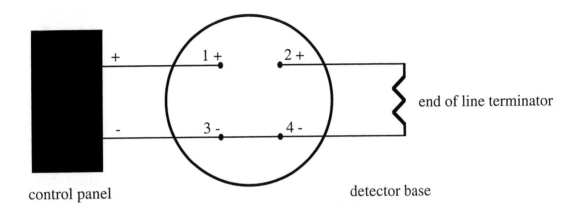

The diagram below shows the detector head **installed** to the base, a **jumper** completes the circuit between 1+ and 2+. If the smoke detector **base** is properly connected into the circuit, the control panel will operate normally when the smoke detector's head is in place, and will indicate trouble when the head is removed.

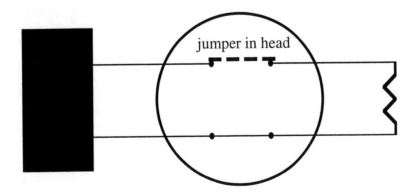

The circuit shown below contains a **trouble contact**. A trouble contact is a NC (normally closed) contact that is **electrically** located **beyond the last** alarm-initiating device and in **series** with the end-of-line device.

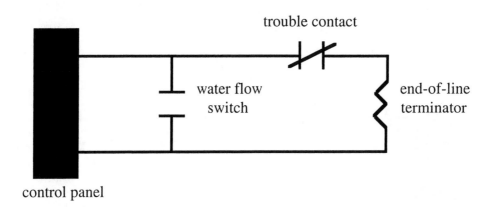

trouble contact

water flow switch

end-of-line terminator

control panel

The function of the trouble contact is to make sure that if someone tampers with the water flow switch, the control panel will indicate trouble. This "tamper switch," as its called, is held mechanically closed by the cover of the water-flow switch. If someone takes the cover off the water-flow switch to tamper with the switch, the tamper switch (trouble contact) opens interrupting the flow of supervisory current and the control panel will indicate such.

The trouble contact is a normally-closed contact in series with the circuit, if the trouble contact opens, every alarm-initiating device that is **electrically beyond** the trouble contact will be disabled. This is the reason the trouble contact must be located electrically in the circuit **beyond the last alarm initiating device.**

In some cases smoke detectors contain a trouble contact. With multi-trouble contacts the circuit is electrically identical to a single-trouble contact circuit. **All** trouble contacts are **electrically beyond** the last alarm-initiating contact, and are in **series** with one another and **electrically ahead** of the end-of-line device.

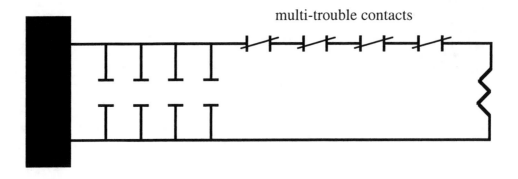

multi-trouble contacts

The "open loop" circuit is a very simple protective loop circuit. All switches are wired in parallel when any switch is closed it will signal the alarm. Current only flows when a signal is being sent.

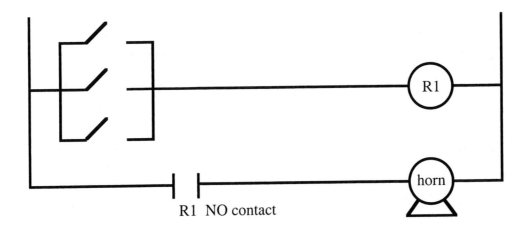

This kind of protective loop is not often used because there is no **supervision** of the circuit.

No supervision means, if a wire would break in the circuit the alarm would receive no signal if an intrusion occurred.

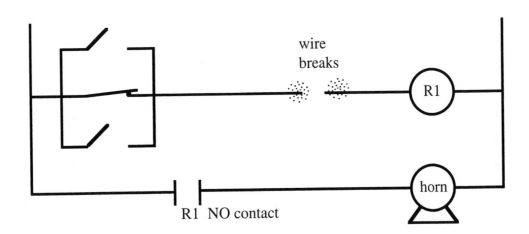

A "closed loop" is used in most alarm systems because it is a **supervised** circuit. In a closed loop circuit current flows continuously, except when the circuit is opened, then a signal is sent to the alarm. In a closed loop circuit the switches are wired in series. A **"single"** closed loop is shown below.

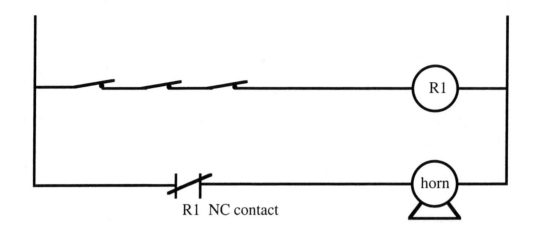

The closed loop circuit shown above has all 3 switches closed to hold voltage on R1 coil, with R1 coil energized the NC (normally closed) contact would be **open** not allowing a signal to the horn.

If an intrusion occurred opening any of the switches R1 would de-energized, R1 NC contact would **close** and send a signal to the horn.

The circuit below shows a wire breaking in the closed loop circuit, this also **would** cause a signal to be sent to the alarm. This is a **supervised** circuit.

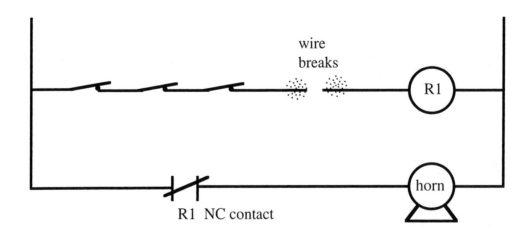

A "single" closed loop is better because it does provide **supervision** of the circuit. The disadvantages are shown below in the diagrams.

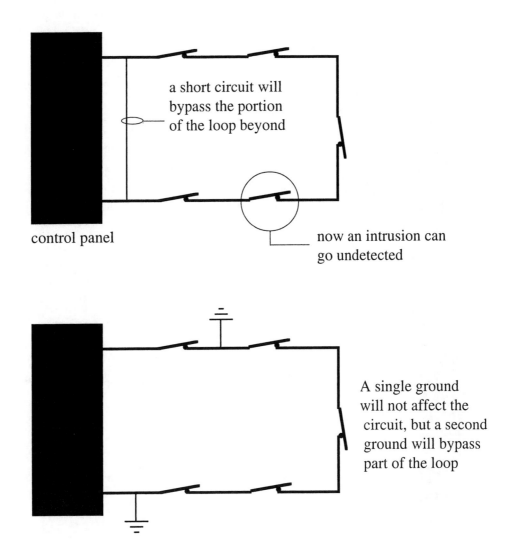

control panel

a short circuit will
bypass the portion
of the loop beyond

now an intrusion can
go undetected

A single ground
will not affect the
circuit, but a second
ground will bypass
part of the loop

As you can see a single accidental ground will give no alarm condition, two or more grounds no alarm condition and an intrusion would go undetected.

The circuit shown below is a end-of-line terminator loop. It can save wiring as it is not necessary to run the end of the loop back to the control panel. A terminator is a simple resistor connected to the far end of the loop. It must **not** be connected in series or in parallel with the loop at the **feed** end (control end) or the system will not work correctly. The correct value of resistance must be used, this is no problem as they usually are provided with the equipment.

The end-of-line terminator (resistor) loop can be triggered by the closing of open circuit devices and by the opening of closed circuit devices. A short across the loop will cause an alarm, an accidental ground on both sides causes an alarm. Two grounds on the **same** side will not cause an alarm.

This loop is fully supervised.

The NFPA 72 Code states: The circuit shall be electrically supervised so that a trouble signal shall indicate the occurrence of a single open or a single ground fault on any installation wiring circuit that would prevent proper alarm operation. Either a trouble or alarm signal shall indicate the occurrence of a multiple ground fault or any short-circuit fault on the fire alarm system primary (main) power supply, alarm initiating, signaling line, or required alarm indicating circuits that would prevent proper alarm operation.

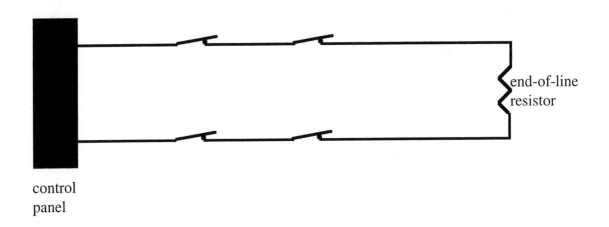

end-of-line
resistor

control
panel

A basic wiring diagram of a circuit is shown below. A **pair** of wires are run from the control panel power source to each switch, even though only the hot wire is cut and connected in series to the switch **both** wires are run to the switch. Manufacturers discourage from only running a single wire to each switch as troubleshooting a single wire circuit can be very time-consuming to say the least, plus the single wire circuit is easier for an intruder to defeat.

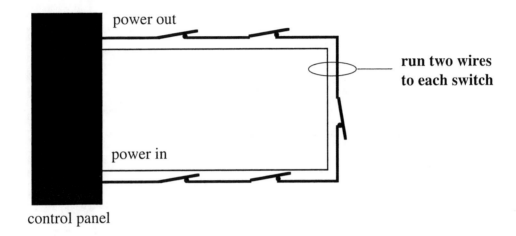

In the circuit below a drop relay (R2) is added to provide a **continuous** alarm until the circuit is manually **reset**.

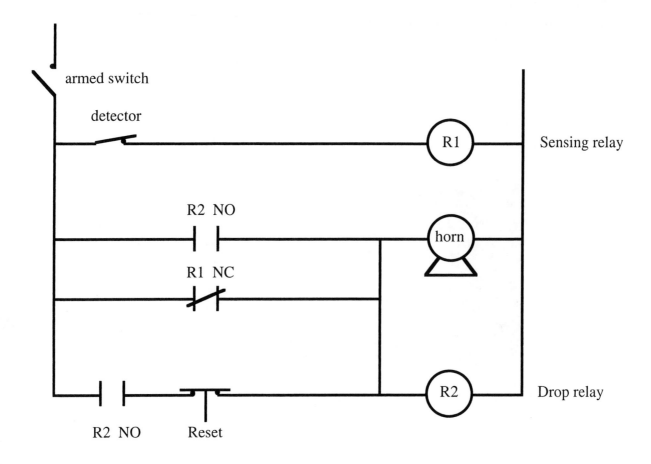

With the detector switch closed R1 coil is energized opening R1 NC contact, as soon as the detector switch is opened R1 coil is de-energized R1 NC closes sending a signal to the horn and also energizing R2 the drop relay closing both R2 NO contacts. One R2 NO contact also sends a signal to the horn, the other R2 NO contact is a **holding circuit** to R2 coil. The detector switch can be **re-closed** and the horn will continue to sound until the reset button has been manually pushed opening the circuit to R2 drop relay.

CLASS 1,2 and 3 CIRCUITS

The circuits in Article 725 are characterized by usage and electrical power limitations which differentiate them from electric light and power circuits.

Due to their power limitations, both Class 2 and 3 circuits consider safety from a fire initiation standpoint. In addition, Class 2 circuits provide acceptable protection from electric shock. However, since Class 3 circuits permit higher allowable levels of voltage and current, additional safeguards are specified to provide protection against the electric shock hazard that could be encountered.

In general, wiring of Class 1 signal systems must be the same as light and power general-purpose wiring and conductors for any Class 1 remote-control, signaling, or power limited circuits must have overcurrent protection.

The advantage of Class 2 wiring is that it carries very few restrictions as to wire size, insulation thickness or material. Fuses or circuit breakers are generally not required. Class 2 and 3 current supply from batteries is considered as providing satisfactory current limitation.

Most control circuits for magnetic starters and contactors could not qualify as Class 2 or 3 circuits because of the high energy required for the coils. Any control circuit over **150 volts** such as 240 volt or 480 volt could not be a Class 2 or 3 circuit.

A remote-control circuit must be a Class 1 circuit if the failure of the circuit would create a hazard.

Code Table 11a shows the power limitations for **AC** Class 2 and 3 circuits.

Table 11b shows the power limitations for **DC** Class 2 and 3 circuits.

CLASS 1

The diagram below shows some of the Class 1 type circuits.

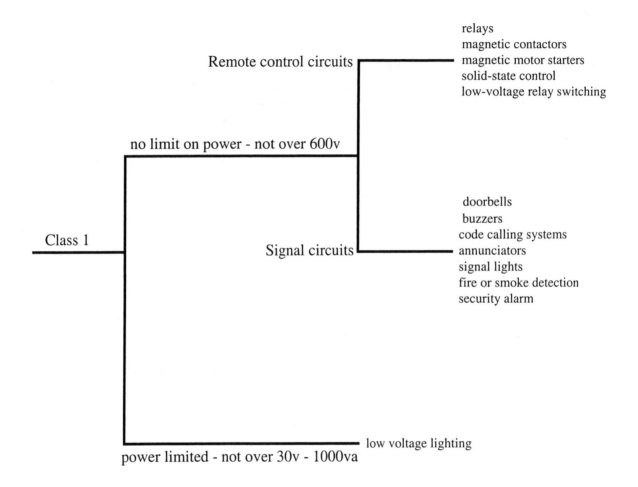

Class 1

no limit on power - not over 600v

Remote control circuits
- relays
- magnetic contactors
- magnetic motor starters
- solid-state control
- low-voltage relay switching

Signal circuits
- doorbells
- buzzers
- code calling systems
- annunciators
- signal lights
- fire or smoke detection
- security alarm

power limited - not over 30v - 1000va
- low voltage lighting

CLASS 2 and 3

The diagram below shows some of the Class 2 and 3 type circuits.

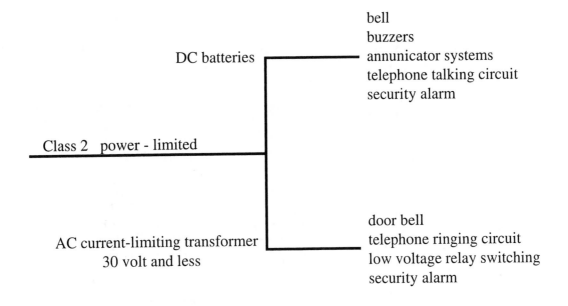

DC batteries

bell
buzzers
annunicator systems
telephone talking circuit
security alarm

Class 2   power - limited

AC current-limiting transformer
30 volt and less

door bell
telephone ringing circuit
low voltage relay switching
security alarm

Class 3   power - limited

above 30 volt to 150 volt

ARTICLE 760

Article 760 covers the installation of wiring and equipment of fire protective signaling systems operating at 600 volts, nominal, or less. Fire protective signaling circuits shall be classified as nonpower-limited or power limited.

Article 760 is divided into four parts:

I.	SCOPE	760.1 - 760.35
II.	NON-POWER LIMITED	760.41 - 760.53
III.	POWER	760.121 - 760.154
IV.	LISTING REQUIREMENTS	760.176 - 760.179

The wiring installation shall be in accordance 110.3(B) and with the appropriate Articles in Chapter 3. Exception: As provided in 760.48 through 760.53.

NON-POWER LIMITED
WIRING INSTALLATION
CATEGORIES

IN CONDUIT
- insulation must be rated 600 volt
- #18 and #16 shall be permitted to be used, provided they do not exceed the ampacities given in Table 402.5.
- #14 and larger shall comply with Article 310
- #18&16 must be approved construction
- multiconductor cable may be used if within compliance

EXPOSED
- circuits operating at 150 volts or less
- listed for the use

PLENUM
- metallic conduit or MC cable per 300.22
- other listed cables for plenum use

SIZE

• copper conductors of #18 and #16 shall be permitted to be used provided they supply loads that do not exceed the ampacities given in Table 402.5 and are installed in a raceway, an approved enclosure, or a listed cable. Conductors **larger** than #16 shall not supply loads greater than the ampacities given in 310.15.

INSULATION

• insulation on conductors shall be rated for 600v. Conductors **larger than** #16 shall comply with Article 310. Conductors in sizes #18 and #16 shall be type KF-2, KFF-2, PAFF, PTFF, PF, PFF, PGF, PGFF, RFH-2, RFHH-2, RFHH-3, SF-2, SFF-2, TF, TFF, TFN, TFFN, ZF, OR ZFF. Other types of conductors are permitted if **listed** for non-power limited fire protective signaling circuit use.

NON-POWER LIMITED

COPPER CONDUCTORS

MATERIALS

• Conductors shall be solid or stranded copper.

MULTICONDUCTOR

CABLE FOR CIRCUITS 150 VOLTS OR LESS

• The multiconductor cable shall be installed in a raceway, exposed on ceilings or sidewalks, or fished in concealed spaces in accordance with the requirements of Chapter 3.

15TH

POWER LIMITED

• Control panel must be listed as having circuits rated as power limited. (UL requirement)

• Terminals in the control panel must be labeled "POWER LIMITED." (NEC 760.124)

• Power limited and non-power limited circuits may not be run in the same conduit unless permitted by 760.136(B) through (G)

• Power limited wire may be used only on power limited circuits

• Power limited wire must not be connected to a non-power limited circuit, even if installed in conduit

• Power limiting may be accomplished by non-tamperable overcurrent protection such as a circuit breaker or fusestat

• Inherently (normally) limited power source. Certain transformers are designed to "fold back." (If secondary leads are shorted, the transformer will not output any power).

• The circuit shall be durably marked where plainly visible at terminations to indicate that it is a power-limited fire protective signaling circuit.

• Power limited circuits can be reclassified and installed as non-power limited circuits if the markings required by section 760.124 are elimated and the entire circuit is installed using the wiring methods and materials in accordance with non-power limited circuits

50 Questions   -   Time Limit   One Hour and 15 minutes

1. The National Electrical Code _____.

(a) is intended to be a design manual
(b) is meant to be used as an instruction manual for untrained persons
(c) is intended to protect persons and property
(d) is published by the Bureau of Standards

2. The N.E.C. covers _____.

I.   installations of electrical conductors, equipment, and raceways within or on public and private buildings or other structures, including mobile homes, recreational vehicles, and floating buildings; and other premises, such as yards, carnivals, parking and other lots, and industrial substations
II.   installations of conductors and equipment that connect to the supply of electricity
III. installations of optic fiber cables

(a) I only   (b) II only   (c) III only   (d) I, II and III

3. The Code rules and provisions are enforced by _____.

(a) the electric utility company that provides the power
(b) the U.S. Government
(c) government bodies exercising legal jurisdiction over electrical installations
(d) U.L.

4. The conductors and equipment required or permitted by this Code shall be acceptable only if _____.

(a) approved   (b) identified   (c) labeled   (d) listed

5. Throughout the Code, the voltage considered shall be that at which the circuit _____.

(a) is grounded   (b) feeds   (c) operates   (d) drops

6. Conductors shall be _____ unless otherwise provided in the Code.

(a) lead   (b) stranded   (c) copper   (d) aluminum

7. Only wiring methods recognized as _____ are included in the Code.

(a) approved   (b) suitable   (c) listed   (d) identified

8. Unless identified for use in the operating environment, no conductors or equipment shall be located in _____ having a deteriorating effect on the conductors or equipment.

I. damp or wet locations   II. where exposed to gases, fumes, vapors, liquids, etc.

(a) I only   (b) II only   (c) both I and II   (d) neither I nor II

9. Electric equipment shall be installed in a neat and _____ manner.

(a) efficient   (b) safe   (c) workmanlike   (d) orderly

10. Unused openings in boxes, raceways, and other enclosures shall be _____.

(a) closed with a device listed for such service with the equipment
(b) effectively closed
(c) closed to afford protection substantially equivalent to the equipment wall
(d) open

11. In all cases the work space in front of electrical equipment shall permit at least a _____ degree opening of equipment doors or hinged panels.

(a) 60   (b) 90   (c) 120   (d) 180

12. Fuses, circuit breakers, or combinations thereof, shall not be connected in parallel except _____.

I. field installed   II. factory assembled and listed as a unit   III. readily accessible

(a) I only   (b) II only   (c) III only   (d) I and III

13. Supplementary overcurrent devices shall not be required to be ____.

(a) accessible   (b) readily accessible   (c) continuous duty   (d) adjustable

14. ____ is defined as properly localizing of an overcurrent condition to restrict outages to the circuit or equipment affected, accomplished by choice of overcurrent protective devices and their ratings or settings.

(a) Monitoring   (b) Coordination   (c) Choice selection   (d) Fault device

15. An overcurrent trip unit of a circuit shall be connected in series with each ____.

(a) ungrounded conductor   (b) grounded conductor
(c) overcurrent device   (d) transformer

16. Overcurrent protection shall be provided in each ____ circuit conductor and shall be located at the point where the conductors receive there supply except as specified in 240.21(A) thru (H).

(a) grounded   (b) ungrounded   (c) grounding   (d) neutral

17. Circuit breakers shall not be located in the vicinity of easily ignitable material such as in ____.

(a) hallways   (b) laundry rooms   (c) clothes closets   (d) basements

18. Enclosures for overcurrent devices in damp or wet locations shall be identified for use in such locations and shall be mounted so there is at least ____ inch air space between the enclosure and the wall or other supporting surface.

(a) 1/4   (b) 3/8   (c) 3/4   (d) 1

19. Fuses and circuit breakers shall be so located or ____ that persons will not be burned or otherwise injured by their operation.

(a) concealed   (b) guarded   (c) shielded   (d) elevated

20. Conductive materials enclosing electrical conductors are grounded to _____.

I. prevent surges of voltage
II. prevent surges of lightning
III. limit the voltage to ground on these materials

(a) I only   (b) II only   (c) III only   (d) I, II and III

21. A system (of two-wire DC) operating at 50v or less between conductors shall _____.

(a) not be grounded   (b) be grounded
(c) not be permitted   (d) not required to be grounded

22. AC circuits of less than 50 volts shall be grounded under which of the following?

I. Where installed outside as overhead conductors.
II. Where supplied by transformers if the transformer supply system is ungrounded.
III. Where supplied by transformers if the transformer supply system exceeds 150 volts to ground.

(a) I only   (b) II only   (c) III only   (d) I, II or III

23. Impedance grounded neutral systems shall be grounded in accordance with 250.36 or _____.

(a) 250.186   (b) 250.37   (c) 250.187   (d) 250.86

24. A grounding electrode conductor shall be required for a system that supplies a _____ and is derived from a transformer not more than 1000 va.

(a) Class 1 circuit   (b) Class 2 circuit   (c) Class 3 circuit   (d) none of these

25. Equipment installed and likely to become energized shall be grounded at which of the following distances?

(a) 8 feet horizontal and 5 feet vertical of grounded metal objects
(b) 5 feet vertical and 5 feet horizontal of grounded metal objects
(c) 8 feet vertical and 5 feet horizontal of grounded metal objects
(d) 8 feet vertical and 8 feet horizontal of grounded metal objects

26. Which of the following statements about grounding conductors is true?

I. Must conduct safely any ground fault current imposed on it.
II. Must have a sufficiently low impedance circuit facilitating the operation of the overcurrent device.

(a) I only   (b) II only   (c) both I and II   (d) neither I nor II

27. The grounding electrode shall be installed such that ____ of length is in contact with the soil.

(a) 6'   (b) 7'   (c) 7' 6"   (d) 8'

28. Bonding together of all separate grounding electrodes will limit ____ between them and between their associated wiring systems.

(a) potential differences   (b) high frequencies   (c) stray currents   (d) arcing

29. Grounding electrode conductors smaller than #6 shall be protected in ____.

I. EMT   II. IMC   III. rigid PVC   IV. rigid metal conduit

(a) I or IV only   (b) I, II or IV only   (c) II or IV only   (d) I, II, III or IV

30. Cases or frames of current transformers, the primaries of which are not over 150 volts to ground and which are used exclusively to supply current to meters ____.

(a) need to be grounded   (b) need to be isolated
(c) need to be insulated   (d) need _not_ be grounded

31. Conductors of AC and DC circuits rated 600 volt or less, shall be permitted to occupy the same conduit if ____.

(a) all conductors shall have an insulation voltage rating equal to at least the maximum circuit
   voltage rating of any conductor in the conduit
(b) all conductors shall have a 600 volt insulation rating
(c) conductors must have a dividing barrier in the raceway
(d) AC and DC are not permitted in the same raceway

32. Cable or raceway that is installed through bored holes in wood members, holes shall be bored so that the edge of the hole is not less than 1 1/4" from the nearest edge of the wood member. Where this distance cannot be maintained the cable or raceway shall be protected from penetration by nails and screws by a steel plate or bushing, at least ____ inch thick, and of appropriate length and width installed to cover the area of wiring.

(a) 1/16   (b) 1/8   (c) 3/16   (d) 1/4

33. At least ____ inches of free conductor shall be left at each outlet and switch point.

(a) 4   (b) 6   (c) 8   (d) 12

34. The number and size of conductors in any raceway shall not be more than will permit ____.

I. ready installation or withdrawal of conductors without damage to the conductors or to their insulation
II. dissipation of the heat

(a) I only   (b) II only   (c) both I and II   (d) neither I nor II

35. Electrical installations in hollow spaces, vertical shafts, and ventilation or air-handling ducts shall be so made that the possible spread of fire or products of combustion will not be ____.

(a) substantially increased   (b) allowed   (c) exposed   (d) underrated

36. Electric equipment with a metal enclosure or electrical equipment with a nonmetallic enclosure listed for the use within an air-handling space and having adequate ____ producing characteristics, and associated wiring material suitable for the ambient temperature shall be permitted to be installed in other space used for environmental air unless prohibited in this Code.

I. fire-resistant   II. low-smoke

(a) I or II   (b) I and II   (c) I only   (d) II only

37. Conductors operating at less than 50 volts and not covered in Articles 411, 517, 551, 552, 650, 669, 690, 725 and 760, shall not be smaller than ____ copper or equivalent.

(a) #16   (b) #18   (c) #14   (d) #12

38. Communication circuits shall be permitted in the same cable with ____ circuits.

I. Class 1   II. Class 2   III. Class 3

(a) I only   (b) I and II   (c) II and III   (d) I, II and III

39. ____ and similar controls used in conjunction with electrically controlled household heating and air-conditioning shall not be considered safety-control equipment.

I. Room thermostats   II. Water temperature regulating devices

(a) I only   (b) II only   (c) both I and II   (d) neither I nor II

40. Class 1 power-limited circuits shall be supplied from a source having a rated output of not more than 30 volts and ____ va.

(a) 100   (b) 300   (c) 500   (d) 1000

41. For Class 1 circuits, the derating factors given in Table 310.15 B3a shall apply only if remote-control or signaling circuits(s) ____.

(a) have more than 3 conductors in a cable or raceway
(b) conductors carry non-continuous loads
(c) have more than 4 conductors in a raceway or cable
(d) conductors carry continuous loads

42. A Class 1 power supply unit shall be durably marked where plainly visible to indicate ____.

I. its electrical rating   II. total va output   III. the temperature class

(a) I only   (b) I and II   (c) I and III   (d) I, II and III

43. Where overcurrent protection is required for Class 1 circuits, the overcurrent protection for a #18 conductor shall not be more than ____.

(a) not be over 5 amps   (b) not be over 7 amps
(c) not be over 10 amps   (d) not be over 15 amps

44. In general, Class 2 control circuits and power circuits _____.

I. may occupy the same raceway   II. shall be installed in different raceways

(a) I only   (b) II only   (c) both I and II   (d) neither I nor II

45. Fire protective signaling circuits shall be grounded, the only exception is DC power-limited circuits having a maximum current of _____ amperes.

(a) 0.300   (b) 1.5   (c) 0.030   (d) 2.34

46. Nonpower-limited fire protective signaling circuits shall _____.

I.   not be more than 600 volts
II. not exceed 7 amps overcurrent protection for #18 conductor
III. be permitted in the same raceway whether AC or DC current

(a) I only   (b) I and II only   (c) II only   (d) I, II and III

47. Power-limited fire protective signaling circuits where installed in exposed cable, located within 7 feet of the floor, cable shall be securely fastened in an approved manner at intervals of not more than _____ inches.

(a) 18   (b) 24   (c) 30   (d) 36

48. Stranded copper in sizes _____ and larger shall be permitted for nonpower-limited fire protective signaling circuits.

(a) #24   (b) #22   (c) #20   (d) #18

49. Conductors of power-limited multiconductor cables shall not be smaller than _____.

(a) #28   (b) #26   (c) #24   (d) #22

50. Which of the following is not a type of optical fiber cable?

(a) AC   (b) nonconductive   (c) conductive   (d) composite

OHMS LAW

Ohm's Law is one of the most important things that you will use throughout your electrical career. It is a mathematical tool which is of the greatest use in determining an **unknown** factor of voltage, current or resistance in an electrical circuit in which the other two factors are known.

It is a simple law that states the relationship between voltage, current and resistance in a mathematical equation.

In electrical terms, voltage is represented by the letter "E", current by the letter "I", and resistance by the letter "R".

The Ohm's Law formula cannot work properly unless all values are expressed in the **correct units** of measurement:

VOLTAGE is always expressed in **VOLTS**

CURRENT is always expressed in **AMPERES**

RESISTANCE is always expressed in **OHMS**

We measure electromotive force in volts, we measure electric current in amps, and we measure resistance in ohms.

Electricity has many more terms that have to do with measurement: **"VOLTS", "AMPS", "OHMS", "WATTS"** and more.

Electrical energy can be generated, not **electricity**. Electricity can be neither created nor destroyed. All matter is composed of electricity.

Electricity was discovered, not invented. The dictionary defines it as "one of the fundamental quantities in nature".

We must first understand how the electrical system functions and then mathematical analysis can follow.

Since you cannot visually **see** the flow of electrons, current, etc. and you need to **see** the relationship between voltage, current, and resistance, let's do it with some **terms** which you are more familiar with, using water.

WATER		ELECTRICITY
PUMP	=	GENERATOR
PIPE		CONDUCTOR
PRESSURE		VOLTAGE
FLOW of GALLONS		AMPERES
RESTRICTION		RESISTANCE

The **generator** is like a **water pump**, the prime mover.

The **conductor** is like the **water pipe**, the larger the conductor, the less the resistance and the more flow.

The **voltage** is like the **water pressure**, the force pushing.

The **amperes** is like the **flow of water**, an amount of current flowing is like the gallons per minute in water.

The **resistance** is like the **restriction** in the water pipe. A reduction in the water pipe size would cause opposition to the amount of gallons per minute, as would the resistor in an electrical circuit. It limits the flow of current.

Watts (power) is expressing the **rate of work** involved; the power required. With water it requires more work to pump water up to a water tower than it would to pump water at ground level. Wattage is the rate at which the electrical energy is changed into another form of energy, such as light or heat. The faster a lamp changes electrical energy, the brighter it will be.

Horsepower (hp) is the unit of measurement for mechanical power which is equal to 33,000 foot-pounds per minute. One horsepower is developed when the product of the distance and pounds equals 33,000 and this is done in **one minute**. In electrical terms, one horsepower = 746 watts. One horsepower is developed if 33,000 pounds are lifted one foot in one minute. This represents the **work** done by the **output** of a motor.

OHM'S LAW DEFINITIONS

(E) VOLT: The practical unit of voltage; the pressure required to force one ampere through a resistance of one ohm. To make electrons flow in a conductor, an electrical pressure must be applied and this is called electromotive force (EMF) or voltage.

(I) AMPERE: The practical unit of electric current flow; the electric current that will flow through one ohm under a pressure of one volt.

(Ω) OHM: The practical unit of electrical resistance; the resistance through which one volt will force one ampere.

(R) RESISTANCE: The opposition which a device or material offers to the flow of current; the opposition which results in the production of heat in the material carrying the current. Resistance is measured in ohms. All resistances have two dimensions: cross-sectional area and length.

(W) POWER: The rate at which electrical energy is delivered and consumed. Power is measured in watts. A motor produces mechanical power measured in horsepower. A heater produces heat (thermal) power. A light bulb produces both heat and light power (usually measured in candlepower).

Electrical power is equal to voltage times the amperage. $\mathbf{W = E \times I}$

Ohm's Law can be stated as "the current flowing in a circuit is directly proportional to the voltage applied to the circuit, and inversely proportional to the resistance of the circuit". **I = E/R**

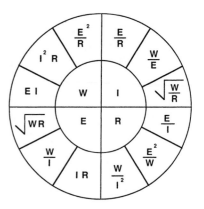

Get into the habit of always sketching out an Ohm's Law circuit **before** trying to solve it.

$\boxed{\textbf{I = E/R}}$ One volt will force one amp through a conductor having a resistance of one ohm.

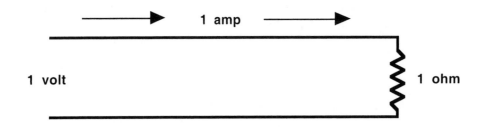

$\boxed{\textbf{I = E/R}}$ If the voltage is increased to 2 volts, the current will be 2 amps through one ohm of resistance.

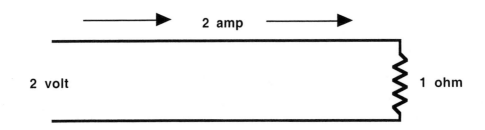

$\boxed{\textbf{I = E/R}}$ If the voltage is increased to 10 volts, the current will be 10 amps through one ohm of resistance.

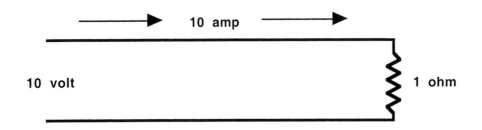

If the resistance is **reduced** to 1/2 ohm, the current would **double** to 20 amps, if the voltage remained at 10 volts.

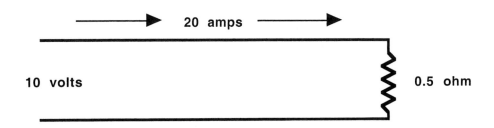

Directly proportional means that one factor will be **increased** in proportion to an **increase** in another factor.

Example: The current increased to 2 amps as the voltage increased to 2 volts, the resistance remained the same, one ohm.

Inversely proportional means that one factor will be **increased** in proportion to a **decrease** in another factor or vice versa.

Example: The current will increase in proportion to a decrease in resistance. The current doubled to 20 amps with a decrease in resistance to 0.5 ohm.

Doubling the cross-sectional area of a conductor will reduce the resistance of the conductor by one-half.

An electric current consists of a complete path for the current from the supply, through the load, and back to the supply. If the current can't get back to the source of supply it will never leave.

Kirchhoff's First Law: The sum of all the currents flowing toward a junction always equals the sum of all the currents flowing away from that junction.

SERIES CIRCUIT

In a series circuit all devices are connected end to end, in a closed path, and the same amount of current flows through each device.

Current flows the <u>same</u> through the series circuit.

If two or more resistances are connected in such a way that they carry the **same** current, they are in **series.**

The series circuit was used in the old-style Christmas lights. Each bulb was rated at 15 volts when used on a 120 volt circuit of eight lights. Each bulb received one-eighth of the total 120 volts or 15 volts. If one bulb burns out, they all go out. Series circuit wiring is impractical for ordinary purposes.

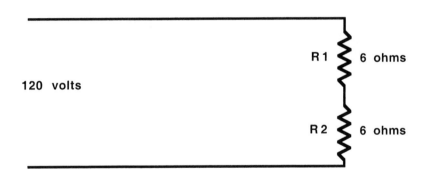

What is the current flowing in this series circuit? The first step is to find the total resistance in the series circuit.

Total resistance in series: R total = R1 + R2
$$6 \text{ ohm} + 6 \text{ ohm} = 12 \text{ ohm}$$

Now apply the Ohm's Law formula for current I = E/R
$$E = 120 \text{ volts} \quad 120v/12 \text{ ohm} = 10 \text{ amps}$$

10 amps is flowing through this series circuit.

With 6 amps of current flowing in this series circuit, what is the applied voltage? The first step is to find the total resistance.

In a series circuit the formula for total resistance is:

$$R \text{ total} = R1 + R2 + R3 \ldots\ldots$$
$$9\ \Omega + 8\ \Omega + 3\ \Omega = 20\ \Omega \text{ total R}$$

Now apply the Ohm's Law formula: $E = I \times R$

The current is 6 amps
6 amps x 20 Ω = 120 volt

120 volt is the applied voltage to this series circuit.

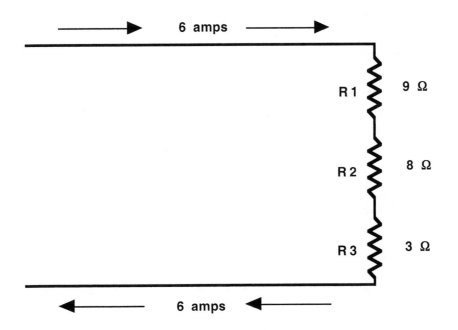

With 11.5 amps flowing in this series circuit, what is the total R?

Apply Ohm's Law formula: R = E/I   115v/11.5a = 10 ohm   R total = 10 ohm

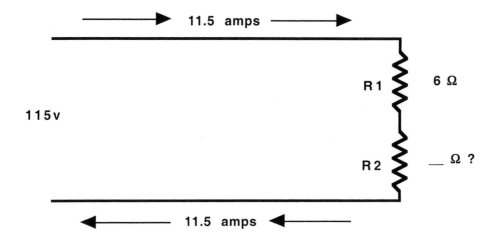

What is the resistance of R2?   10 ohm -6 ohm = 4 ohm   R2 = 4 ohm

What is the voltage at R1?   Apply Ohm's Law formula: E = I x R   11.5a x 6 Ω = 69 volts

What is the voltage at R2?   E = I x R   11.5 amp x 4 Ω = 46 volts

** **Checkpoint:**   69 volts + 46 volts = 115v (the applied voltage)

Current flows the **<u>same</u>** in a series circuit. It takes 115 volts to push 11.5 amps through 10 ohms of resistance.

Kirchhoff's Voltage Law: The sum of the voltage drops around a circuit is equal to the source voltage.

PARALLEL CIRCUITS

If the **same** voltage exists across **each** load, the circuit is connected in parallel.

Each load is connected in a branch across the voltage source. Each branch current depends on the load resistance in that branch, so the total current in parallel is the current of each branch added collectively:

I total = I1 + I2 + I3 ....

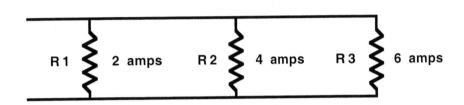

What is the current flowing in this parallel circuit?   I total = 2 amps + 4 amps + 6 amps = 12 amps

When more loads are connected into a **series** circuit, the total resistance **increases.**

When more loads are connected into a **parallel** circuit, the total resistance **decreases.**

A picture of this is worth a thousand words, using water for the series and parallel loads:

SERIES CIRCUIT HAS ONLY ONE PATH
                               PARALLEL CIRCUIT HAS MORE THAN ONE PATH

 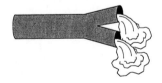

The total resistance in parallel in **less** than one resistance because each load has its own source of supply, the series circuit has only one supply for all the loads.

EQUAL PARALLEL RESISTANCE

Its very easy to find the total resistance in parallel when all resistances are **equal.**

Apply this formula: <u>RESISTANCE OF ONE RESISTOR</u>
                                 NUMBER OF RESISTORS IN PARALLEL

Example: What is the total resistance in the following circuit?

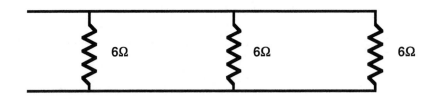

R total = <u>6 Ω</u>   = 2 Ω total resistance
                3 resistors

Example: What is the total resistance in the following circuit?

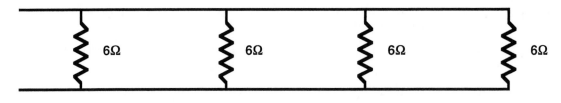

R total = <u>6 Ω</u>   = 1.5 Ω total resistance
                4 resistors

As you can see, everytime you add a resistance in **parallel** the total resistance is **less.**

Checkpoint: The total resistance in parallel is always **less than the **smallest** resistor in the parallel circuit.

UNEQUAL PARALLEL RESISTANCE

Finding the total resistance for **unequal** resistors is not as easy as for equal resistors.

Example: Find the total resistance for the following circuit.

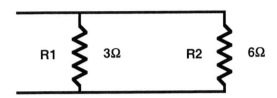

One formula for total resistance in a parallel circuit is: $1/Rt = 1/R1 + 1/R2$

$1/3 + 1/6$ The common denominator is 6.
$2/6 + 1/6 = 3/6$ Now invert $6/3 = 2$ ohm total resistance

Checkpoint: Remember the total resistance in parallel is **less than any one resistance. So the total resistance has to be less than R1 which is 3 ohms.

Another formula to find total resistance is:

$\dfrac{R1 \times R2}{R1 + R2}$ $R1 = 3\ \Omega$ $R2 = 6\ \Omega$ $\dfrac{3 \times 6}{3 + 6}$ $= \dfrac{18}{9}$ $= 2$ ohm total resistance

By using either formula you will get the **same** answer, 2 ohms total resistance, which is **less** than any one resistance.

Next we will use the formulas to find the total resistance for **three** unequal resistors in parallel.

What is the total resistance for the following circuit?

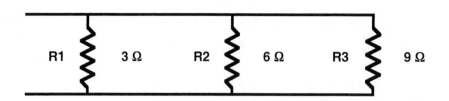

$1/R_t = 1/R_1 + 1/R_2 + 1/R_3$

To find the common denominator multiply R1 x R2. If R3 will divide **equally** that will be the common denominator.

3 x 6 = 18/9 = 2 (divides equally)   So 18 is the common denominator

$$\frac{1}{3} + \frac{1}{6} + \frac{1}{9}$$

$$\overline{18} + \overline{18} + \overline{18}$$

$$\frac{6}{18} + \frac{3}{18} + \frac{2}{18} = \frac{11}{18}$$ invert to 18/11 = ⟦1.63 ohms total resistance⟧

Now apply the other formula. For 3 resistors the formula would be:

$$\frac{R1 \times R2}{R1 + R2} = Y \qquad \frac{Y \times R3}{Y + R3} = R\ total$$

$R1 = 3\,\Omega$ $R2 = 6\,\Omega$ $R3 = 9\,\Omega$

$$\frac{3 \times 6}{3 + 6} = \frac{18}{9} = 2 \qquad Y = 2 \qquad \frac{2 \times 9}{2 + 9} = \frac{18}{11} = ⟦1.63\ ohms\ total\ resistance⟧$$

Checkpoint: The total resistance of 1.63 ohms is the same using either formula and is **less** than the smallest resistor of 3 ohms.

Here is another way to find the total resistance in parallel for unequal resistors using your **calculator**.

Let's use the same resistors 3 Ω, 6 Ω and 9 Ω and see if we get the same answer of 1.63 Ω R total.

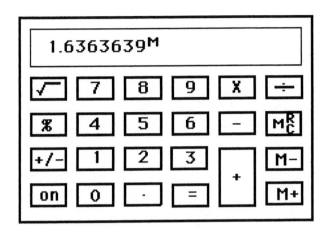

Simply follow this steps:

Using your calculator, clear it so it reads 0. Make sure it does **not** read 0.M

Press 1 Press ÷ Press 3 Press M+   Your calculator should read 0.3333333M

Press 1 Press ÷ Press 6 Press M+   Your calculator should read 0.1666666M

Press 1 Press ÷ Press 9 Press M+   Your calculator should read 0.1111111M

Press 1 Press ÷ Press MRc Press =   Your calculator should read 1.6363639M

On some calculators this button will be shown as:

RM or MR or R·CM

The numbers 3 6 9 are for the unequal resistors of 3 Ω, 6 Ω, and 9 Ω. By using your calculator you can calculate the total resistance for as many resistors as the circuit would have by simply following this format. The **final step** is always :

Press 1 Press ÷ Press MRc Press =   Your calculator should read the **ANSWER.**

Practice this calculator drill a few times, it can be very helpful in determining total resistance in a parallel circuit with **unequal** resistors.

Find the total resistance in the following parallel circuit having four unequal resistors.

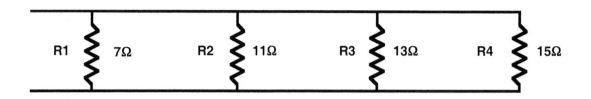

Formula: $1/Rt = 1/R1 + 1/R2 + 1/R3 + 1/R4$

Find the common denominator: $7 \times 11 \times 13 \times 15 = 15,015$

The common denominator is 15,015.

$$\frac{1}{7} + \frac{1}{11} + \frac{1}{13} + \frac{1}{15}$$

$$\frac{2145}{15015} + \frac{1365}{15015} + \frac{1155}{15015} + \frac{5666}{15015} \quad \text{invert} \quad \frac{15015}{5666} = \boxed{2.65 \text{ ohms total resistance}} - - -$$

Using the other formula:

$$\frac{R1 \times R2}{R1 + R2} = Y \quad \frac{Y \times R3}{Y + R3} = Z \quad \frac{Z \times R4}{Z + R4} = Rt$$

$R1 = 7$ $R2 = 11$ $R3 = 13$ $R4 = 15$

$$\frac{7 \times 11}{7 + 11} = \frac{77}{18} = 4.28 \quad Y = 4.28 \quad \frac{4.28 \times 13}{4.28 + 13} = \frac{55.64}{17.28} = 3.22 \quad Z = 3.22 \quad \frac{3.22 \times 15}{3.22 + 15} = \frac{48.3}{18.22} = \boxed{2.65\Omega}$$

Now let's try the calculator drill

Press ⬚1⬚ Press ⬚÷⬚ Press ⬚7⬚ Press ⬚M+⬚
Press ⬚1⬚ Press ⬚÷⬚ Press ⬚11⬚ Press ⬚M+⬚
Press ⬚1⬚ Press ⬚÷⬚ Press ⬚13⬚ Press ⬚M+⬚
Press ⬚1⬚ Press ⬚÷⬚ Press ⬚15⬚ Press ⬚M+⬚
Press ⬚1⬚ Press ⬚÷⬚ Press ⬚MＲＣ⬚ Press ⬚=⬚ Your calculator should read ⬚2.6500195ᴹ⬚

** **Checkpoint:** When working calculations always work the calculation by more than one formula to check yourself for accuracy.

In practical wiring applications we are connecting lights in parallel circuits.

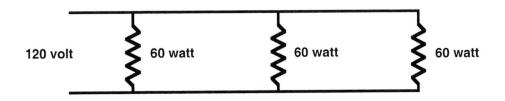

What is the total current in this parallel circuit?

Apply the Ohm's Law formula: I = W/E   60 watt/120 volt = 0.5 amp per light

I total =   I1 + I2 + I3   0.5a + 0.5a + 0.5a = 1.5 amp (I total)

What is the resistance of one light?

Apply Ohm's Law formula: $R = E^2/W$ 120v x 120v/60 watt = 240 Ω each light

What is the total resistance of this parallel circuit?

Use the formula for **equal** resistors in parallel:

$$\frac{\text{Resistance of one resistor}}{\text{Number of resistors in parallel}} \quad = \frac{240\ \Omega}{3\ \text{resistances}} \quad = 80 \text{ ohms R total}$$

OHMS LAW QUESTIONS

1. The number of watts of heat given off by a resistor is expressed by the formula I^2R. If 10 volts is applied to a 5 Ω resistor, the heat given off will be ____ watts.

(a) 500   (b) 250   (c) 50   (d) 20

2. For a given line voltage, four heater coils will consume the most power when connected ____.

(a) all in series
(b) all in parallel
(c) with two parallel pairs in series
(d) one pair in parallel with the other two in series

3. ____ is the ability of a material to permit the flow of electrons.

(a) Voltage   (b) Current   (c) Resistance   (d) Conductance

4. A coil has 100 turns. A current of 10 amps is passed through the coil. The coil develops ____.

(a) 1000 watts   (b) 1 kva   (c) mutual inductance   (d) 1000 amp turns

5. The basic unit of electrical work is the ____.

(a) volt-amp   (b) watt   (c) volt   (d) kva

6. The voltage lost across a portion of a circuit is called the ____.

(a) power factor   (b) I^2R loss   (c) voltage drop   (d) impedance

7. In a series circuit ____ is common.

(a) voltage
(b) wattage
(c) current
(d) resistance

8. Three 9 Ω resistors connected in parallel have a total resistance of ___ ohms.

(a) 3 (b) 9 (c) 27 (d) none of these

9. When a current leaves its intended path and returns to the source, bypassing the load, the circuit is ____.

(a) open (b) shorted (c) incomplete (d) broken

10. Ohm's Law is ____.

(a) an equation for determining power
(b) a measurement of the I^2R losses
(c) the relationship between voltage, current and power
(d) the relationship between voltage, current and resistance

11. A 1000 watt, 120 volt lamp uses electrical energy at the same rate as a ____ ohm resistor.

(a) 10 (b) 14.4 (c) 16.2 (d) 21

12. It is customary to speak of the electromotive force as the ____ of the circuit.

(a) current (b) voltage (c) wattage (d) resistance

13. The total opposition to current flow in an AC circuit is expressed in ohms and called ____.

(a) impedance (b) conductance (c) reluctance (d) resistance

14. The potential difference between two conductors is its ____.

(a) voltage (b) current (c) resistance (d) wattage

15. If the applied voltage to a heat strip is reduced, the current will ____.

(a) increase (b) decrease (c) remain the same (d) none of these

16. A 10 Ω resistance carrying 10 amperes of current uses _____ watts of power.

(a) 100   (b) 200   (c) 500   (d) 1000

17. The total resistance of four 10 Ω resistances in parallel is _____ ohms.

(a) 5   (b) 2.5   (c) 6   (d) 40

18. The most heat is created when current flows through which of the following?

(a) a 10 Ω condenser
(b) a 10 Ω inductance coil
(c) a 10 Ω resistor
(d) heat would be equal

19. Which of the following statements is incorrect?

(a) current flowing through a conductor causes heat
(b) the metal conduit of an electrical system should be grounded
(c) voltmeters are connected in parallel in the circuit
(d) rectifiers change DC to AC

20. Two resistors, a 4 Ω and an 8 Ω are connected in series; the total voltage dropped across both resistors is 12 volts. What is the current through the 4 Ω resistor?

(a) 1 amp   (b) 2 amps   (c) 4 amps   (d) 8 amps

21. When resistors are connected in series, the total resistance is _____.

(a) the sum of the individual resistance values
(b) the equivalent of the smallest resistance value
(c) the equivalent of the largest resistance value
(d) less than the value of the smallest resistance

22. A 1500 watt load is rated @ 230 volts, What would be the wattage if it was connected to a 208 volt source?

(a) 1500 watt   (b) 1350 watt   (c) 1240 watt   (d) 1227 watt

23. Two 500 watt lamps connected in series across a 110 volt line draws 2 amperes. The total power consumed is ____ watts.

(a) 50   (b) 150   (c) 220   (d) 1000

24. A 15 ohm resistance carrying 20 amperes of current uses ____ watts of power.

(a) 300   (b) 3000   (c) 6000   (d) none of these

25. The following circuit has dry cell batteries @ 1.5 volts each. What is the voltage between A and B?

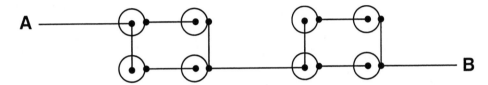

(a) 1.5 volt   (b) 4 volts   (c) 6 volts   (d) 12 volts

VOLTAGE DROP

The resistance of the circuit conductors causes a **voltage drop** to the source voltage. How much the source voltage drops depends on the load and the resistance in the circuit.

Voltage Drop = I x R

The voltage drop in a conductor is a **percentage** of the source voltage. If conductors had **zero resistance**, there would be no voltage drop between the load and the source. This is not possible as all matter has resistance.

The voltage at the **load** can never be the same as the **applied source voltage** due to the resistance of the conductors.

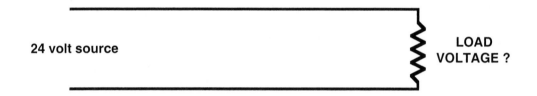

24 volt source   LOAD
                                                                   VOLTAGE ?

Voltage drop can be defined as **wasted work in heating the conductors.**

A larger size conductor in circular-mil area will have a lower resistance and less voltage drop.

Voltage drop in a circuit can be designed from a practical wiring standpoint not to exceed a certain **percentage** of the applied source voltage.

The Code recommends a branch-circuit voltage drop of not more than 3% of the applied source voltage.

A 1% drop in voltage to an incandescent bulb reduces the light output about 3%; A 10% voltage drop will decrease the output about 30%.

The source voltage for alarms usually is 6 volt or 12 volt from batteries, fire alarms may use 24 volt.

PERMITTED VOLTAGE DROP AT 3%

6v x 3% = **0.18v**   12v x 3% = **0.36v**   24v x 3% = **0.72v**   120v x 3% = **3.6v**

In good design, the voltage drop is held to no more than one percent.

Conductors should be sized for voltage drop on the basis of the **maximum possible loading**.

Most alarm systems use two-wire #22 or #24 AWG. A #18 is adequate for bells or sirens if the distance is 40 feet or less, some circuits require a #16 or #14 AWG.

Smaller conductors have negligible self-inductance, and therefore there is no difference to between the resistance of such conductors to DC and their resistance to AC.

Conductor resistances are found in Chapter 9 Table 8 NEC for DC resistances.

| | | CONDUCTORS | | | | DC Ω @ 75° C (167° F) | | |
| | | STRANDING | | OVERALL | | COPPER | | ALUMINUM |
SIZE AWG	AREA CM	Quantity	Diameter Inch	Diameter Inch	Area Inch²	Uncoated Ω / KFT	Coated Ω / KFT	Ω / KFT
18	1620	1	———	0.040	0.001	7.77	8.08	12.8
18	1620	7	0.015	0.046	0.002	7.95	8.45	13.1
16	2580	1	———	0.051	0.002	4.89	5.08	8.05
16	2580	7	0.019	0.058	0.003	4.99	5.29	8.21
14	4110	1	———	0.064	0.003	3.07	3.19	5.06
14	4110	7	0.024	0.073	0.004	3.14	3.26	5.17
12	6530	1	———	0.081	0.005	1.93	2.01	3.18
12	6530	7	0.030	0.092	0.006	1.98	2.05	3.25
10	10380	1	———	0.102	0.008	1.21	1.26	2.00
10	10380	7	0.038	0.116	0.011	1.24	1.29	2.04

1 = solid wire
7 = stranded wire

Ohms resistance per 1000 feet

Circular-mil area

Area square inch for a **bare** conductor

Using the formula VD = I x R, calculate the voltage drop in the circuit below.

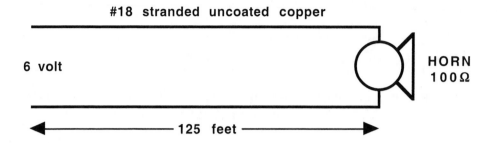

#18 stranded uncoated copper

6 volt

HORN
100Ω

← 125 feet →

First step is to find the resistance for the 250 feet of wire.

Table 8 shows a resistance of 7.95 Ω per 1000 feet of wire.

7.95 Ω x .250 feet = 1.9875 Ω resistance for 250 feet of #18 stranded

Next find the current: I = E/R   6v/100Ω = .06 amp current

VD = I x R   .06a x 1.9875Ω = **0.11925 volts dropped**

The Code recommends not to exceed 3% VD on a branch circuit which would be 6v x 3% = 0.18v

Check the percentage this circuit is dropping:

$$PERCENT \ of \ VOLTAGE \ DROP = \frac{VOLTAGE \ DROP}{APPLIED \ VOLTAGE} = \frac{.11925 \ VD}{6 \ volt} = .019875 \ or \ 2\%$$

Calculate the voltage drop in this same circuit using a #16 stranded uncoated copper conductor.

Table 8 shows a resistance of 4.99 Ω for 1000 feet of #16 wire

4.99Ω x .250 feet = 1.2475 Ω resistance for 250 feet #16

VD = I x R   .06a x 1.2475Ω = **0.07485 volts dropped**

$$Percentage \ of \ voltage \ drop = \frac{.07485v}{6 \ volt} = .012475 \ or \ 1\%$$

VOLTAGE DROP FORMULAS

To find:

VOLTAGE DROP ...... $VD = \dfrac{2 \times K \times D \times I}{CM}$ (or) $VD = I \times R$

WIRE SIZE .... $CM = \dfrac{2 \times \textcircled{K} \times D \times I}{VD \text{ permitted}}$

DISTANCE .... $D = \dfrac{CM \times VD \text{ permitted}}{2 \times K \times I}$

LOAD .... $I = \dfrac{CM \times VD \text{ permitted}}{2 \times K \times D}$

* The "2" in the formulas is for single-phase circuits, this is the conductor to and from the load

* For 3 phase voltage drop calculations, change the "2" in the formula to **1.732**

* "K" is the resistance of a circular mil-foot. Exact $K = \dfrac{R \times CM}{1000'}$

* When using the formula to find "WIRE SIZE" use the **approximate** $\textcircled{K}$ **factor** of 12.9 for copper and 21.2 for aluminum

* "D" is the distance **one way** in a circuit

* "I" is the load in amperes. For motors use the Full Load Current from the motor tables

* "CM" is the size of conductor in circular mils, found only in Table 8

* "VD permitted" is the **percentage of the applied source voltage,** 3% of the source for a branch circuit.

Using the formula "WIRE SIZE" determine what size conductor would be required for the branch circuit below.

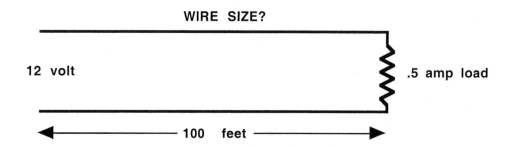

WIRE SIZE?

12 volt

.5 amp load

← 100 feet →

$$\text{WIRE SIZE} \dots\dots \text{CM} = \frac{2 \times \textcircled{K} \times D \times I}{\text{VD permitted}} \qquad \text{CM} = \frac{2 \times 12.9 \times 100' \times .5 \text{ amp}}{.36v \ (3\% \text{ of } 12v)} = 3583 \text{ CM}$$

Turn to Table 8 and select a conductor that has **at least** 3583 CM, this would be a **#14** conductor that has a circular-mil area of 4110.

Using the formula for "DISTANCE" calculate how far this same circuit could be run on a #14 stranded uncoated copper wire without exceeding the Code recommendations.

$$\text{DISTANCE} \dots. D = \frac{\text{CM} \times \text{VD permitted}}{2 \times K \times I}$$

First step is to find the exact K for a #14 stranded uncoated copper wire.

$$\text{Exact K} = \frac{R \times CM}{1000'} = \frac{3.14 \ \Omega \times 4110 \text{ CM}}{1000 \text{ feet}} = 12.9054 \text{ exact K factor}$$

$$D = \frac{4110 \text{ CM} \times .36v \ (3\% \text{ of } 12v)}{2 \times 12.9054 \times .5 \text{ amp}} = \textbf{114.6 feet}$$

Using the formula "LOAD" calculate the maximum current the Code would allow on the branch circuit below.

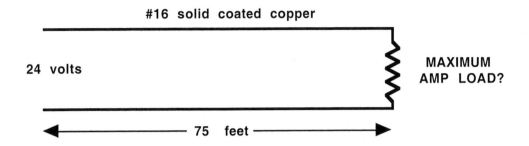

LOAD .... $I = \dfrac{CM \times VD \text{ permitted}}{2 \times K \times D}$

First step is to find exact K for a #16 solid coated copper wire.

Exact $K = \dfrac{R \times CM}{1000'} = \dfrac{5.08\ \Omega \times 2580\ CM}{1000 \text{ feet}} = 13.1064$

$I = \dfrac{2580\ CM \times .72v\ (3\% \text{ of } 24v)}{2 \times 13.1064 \times 75 \text{ feet}} = $ **.94 amp maximum current**

VOLTAGE DROP QUESTIONS

1. What is the resistance of 40 feet of #18 solid uncoated copper wire?

(a) 7.77 Ω   (b) 3.108 Ω   (c) 0.3108 Ω   (d) 0.3232 Ω

2. How far from a 12 volt source can you install a #16 solid coated copper conductor, if the branch circuit load is 0.75 amp?

(a) 30 - 40 feet   (b) 41 - 50 feet   (c) 51 - 75 feet   (d) none of these

3. What size copper conductor is required to a 1.5 amp load, 75 feet from the 24 volt source?

(a) #18   (b) #16   (c) #14   (d) #12

4. A #16 stranded uncoated copper conductor has a total resistance of 0.43 Ω. What is the approximate length of this conductor?

(a) 50 - 75 feet   (b) 76 - 90 feet   (c) 91 - 120 feet   (d) none of these

5. What is the voltage drop in a branch circuit to a siren that has a 50 Ω load? The source voltage is 6 volt, the distance is 40 feet, the conductor is #14 solid uncoated copper.

(a) .014   (b) .029   (c) .044   (d) .056

6. What is the total resistance of two #16 solid uncoated copper conductors? Each is 85 feet in length and connected together in parallel.

(a) 0.41565 Ω   (b) 4.1565 Ω   (c) 0.207825 Ω   (d) none of these

7. What is the maximum load in amps the Code allows for a branch circuit using #18 solid coated copper wire? 12 volt source, 65 feet in distance.

 (a) .12 - .24 amp   (b) .25 - .36 amp   (c) .37 - .50 amp   (d) none of these

8. What size copper conductor is required for a branch circuit to a horn that has a .25 amp load? Source voltage is 6 volt, the distance is 50 feet.

(a) #18   (b) #16   (c) #14   (d) #12

9. Find the approximate distance between the source and the load if a #18 stranded uncoated copper conductor is used and the total conductor resistance is 1.05 Ω.

(a) 156 feet   (b) 132 feet   (c) 66 feet   (d) 47 feet

10. What is the voltage drop in a branch circuit that has a .36 amp load? The source voltage is 24 volt, the distance is 56 feet, the conductor is #14 stranded uncoated copper.

(a) .063   (b) .126   (c) .252   (d) .514

CONDUIT FILL

Area of square inches

Chapter 9 Tables and Examples

A. Tables
Notes to Tables

1. See Informative Annex C for the maximum number of conductors and fixture wires, all of the same size (total cross-sectional area including insulation) permitted in trade sizes of the applicable conduit or tubing.

2. Table 1 applies only to complete conduit or tubing systems and are not intended to apply to sections of conduit or tubing used to protect exposed wiring from physical damage.

3. Equipment grounding or bonding conductors, when installed, shall be included when calculating conduit or tubing fill. The actual dimensions of the equipment grounding or bonding conductor (insulated or bare) shall be used in the calculation.

4. When conduit or tubing nipples having a maximum length not to exceed 24 inches are installed between boxes, cabinets, and similar enclosures, the nipple shall be permitted to be filled 60 percent of its cross-sectional area, and section 310.15(B)(3)(a) does not apply to this condition.

Note 7. Where the calculated number of conductors, all of the same size, includes a decimal fraction, the next higher whole number shall be used where this decimal is 0.8 or larger.

Note 8. When bare conductors are permitted by other sections of this Code, the dimensions for bare conductors in Table 8 of Chapter 9 shall be permitted.

Note 9. A multiconductor cable or flexible cord of two or more conductors shall be treated as a single conductor cable for calculating percentage conduit fill area. For cables that have elliptical cross section, the cross-sectional area calculation shall be based on using the major diameter of the ellipse as a circle diameter.

   Table C1 is for fixture wires installed in EMT, **many of the conductor insulations used in alarm wiring are listed in this Table C1.**   Table C1 is 40% fill based on **individual** diameters.

   Tables C1 through C12A are also for building wire insulations, conductors **all the same size.**

   When **mixing different size wires and insulations** in a conduit, Table 4 and Table 5 must be used for the calculation.

Most conductor insulations used in alarm wiring such as RFH-2, TF, TFN, PF, PGF, SFF-2, ZF, KF-2, etc. are listed in Table C1 of the Code.

Example: How many #18 TFFN conductors can you install in a 3/4" EMT conduit?

Table C1 shows **38** can be installed in a 3/4" EMT conduit.

Table C1 can be used **if all the conductors** in the EMT conduit have the **same insulation** and are the same AWG **size**. When mixing different size conductors in a conduit Table 4 and Table 5 must be used.

TABLE 4 - Electrical Metallic Tubing

Trade Size	Internal Diameter Inches	Area - Square Inches				
			Not Lead Covered			
		Total 100%	2 Cond. 31%	Over 2 Cond. 40%	Nipple Fill 60%	1 Cond. 53%
1/2		0.304		.122	.182	
3/4		0.533		.213	.320	
1		0.864		.346	.519	
1 1/4		1.496		.598	.897	
1 1/2		2.036		.814	1.221	
2		3.356		1.342	2.013	
2 1/2		5.858		2.343	3.515	
3		8.846		3.538	5.307	
3 1/2		11.545		4.618	6.927	
4		14.753		5.901	8.852	

A 1/2" conduit has a cross-sectional area of .304, three conductors can fill 40% of this area or .122. A 1/2" nipple (24" or less) can be filled 60% or .182.

A single conductor can fill the csa 53%, two conductors 31%.

Table 5 below shows the approximate area of square inch for each conductor insulation. For a **bare** conductor the area of square inch is found in Table 8.

Size AWG kcmil	Types TFN Approx. Area Sq. In.	Types SF-2 Approx. Area Sq. In.
18	.0055	.0115
16	.0072	.0139

TABLE 4 - Electrical Metallic Tubing

Trade Size	Internal Diameter Inches	Area - Square Inches				
			Not Lead Covered			
		Total 100%	2 Cond. 31%	Over 2 Cond. 40%	Nipple Fill 60%	1 Cond. 53%
1/2		0.304		.122	.182	
3/4		0.533		.213	.320	
1		0.864		.346	.519	
1 1/4		1.496		.598	.897	
1 1/2		2.036		.814	1.221	

Example : What size conduit is required for 20 - #18 TFN and 32 - #16 SF-2 conductors?

Table 5: #18 TFN = .0055 sq.in. x 20 = .11 sq.in.
#16 SF-2 = .0139 sq.in. x 32 = .4448
.5548 sq.in. required

Table 4: Over 2 conductors 40% Fill
1" conduit can be filled to .346 sq.in.
1 1/4" conduit can be filled to .598 sq.in. | ANSWER 1 1/4" |

CONDUIT FILL EXAM QUESTIONS

1. What is the total cross-sectional area of a 3/4" EMT conduit?

(a) .533   (b) .318   (c) .21   (d) .053

2. The area of allowable fill of a 1 1/4" EMT conduit nipple is ____ square inch.

(a) 1.38   (b) 1.5   (c) .6   (d) .897

3. What size EMT conduit is required for the following conductors?

  14 - #16 TF
  16 - #16 TFN
  12 - #14 THHN
   1 - #14 bare solid

(a) 1"   (b) 1 1/4"   (c) 1 1/2"   (d) 2"

4. How many #14 ZF conductors can you install in a 3/4" EMT conduit?

(a) 14   (b) 25   (c) 26   (d) 42

5. What length of nipple may utilize 60% cross-sectional conductor fill?

(a) 30"   (b) 25"   (c) 24"   (d) none of these

6. The approximate area of square inch for a #16 PGF conductor is ____ sq.in.

(a) .0052   (b) .0062   (c) .0660   (d) .0075

NFPA
72

NATIONAL FIRE ALARM CODE

NFPA 72 NATIONAL FIRE ALARM CODE

1. The responsibility for inspections, tests, and maintenance programs shall be assigned by the ____ to a designated person of authority.

(a) fire chief (b) authority having jurisdiction (c) property or building owner (d) fire marshal

2. Room sizes and contours, airflow patterns, obstructions, and other characteristics of the ____ shall be taken into account.

(a) ventilating system   (b) protected hazard   (c) building   (d) structure

3. Interconnection means shall be arranged so that a/an ___ does not cause an alarm signal.

I. single break   II. single ground fault   III. single switch

(a) I only (b) II only (c) III only (d) I & II only

4. In one and two family dwelling units, smoke alarms shall be installed in ___.

   I.   all sleeping rooms and guest rooms
   II.   outside each separate sleeping area within 21 feet of any door to a sleeping room
   III. on each level of the dwelling unit
   IV.   basements

(a) I or II only   (b) II and III only   (c) I and III only   (d) I, II, III and IV

5. Heat sensing fire detectors of the fixed temperature or rate compensated, spot type shall be classified as to the ___ of operation and marked with a color code.

(a) mounting slope   (b) height   (c) mode   (d) temperature

6. A ____ signal shall take precedence over all other signals, except as permitted by 10.6.1 or 10.6.3.

(a) fire alarm   (b) trouble   (c) maintenance   (d) supervisory

7. One of the most critical factors of any fire alarm system is the ____ the fire detecting devices.

(a) location of   (b) spacing between   (c) ambient around   (b) none of these

8. For single and multiple station alarms and household fire alarm systems, all electrical systems designed to be installed by other than a qualified electrician shall be powered from a source NOT in excess of ___ volts that meets the requirements of Article 760 of the NEC.

(a) 12 (b) 24 (c) 30 (d) 120

9. If batteries are used as a source of energy, they shall be replaced ____.

(a) once a year (b) each 6 months (c) every 2 years (d) as recommended

10. The typical average ambient sound level for a residential occupancy is ___.

(a) 70 (b) 55 (c) 40 (d) 35

11. Manual fire alarm boxes shall be located within ___ feet of the exit doorway.

(a) 2 (b) 4 (c) 5 (d) 12

12. A spot type heat sensing detector mounted on the side wall should have the top of the detector ____ inches from the ceiling.

(a) four (b) ten (c) twelve (d) three

13. Smoke detectors shall be installed ____.

I. outside each separate sleeping area
II. in basements
III. on each additional story of the family living unit

(a) I only (b) II only (c) III only (d) I, II and III

14. In a household fire alarm system with rechargeable battery as the primary power source, the battery with proper charging be able to power the alarm for a life of ___.

(a) 6 months (b) 1 year (c) 3 years (d) 5 years

15. A ceiling in which the high point is at one side with the slope extending toward the opposite side is a ___ ceiling.

(a) sloping smooth
(b) sloping peaked
(c) sloping shed
(d) none of these

16. A ceiling in which the ceiling slopes in two directions from the highest point. Curved or domed ceilings can be considered peaked with the slope figured as the slope of the chord from highest to lowest point is considered a _____ type ceiling.

(a) sloping smooth
(b) sloping peaked
(c) sloping shed
(d) none of these

17. When the runner is not in attendance at the proprietary supervising station, the runner shall establish two way communications with the station at intervals not exceeding _____ minutes.

(a) 15 (b) 30 (c) 45 (d) 60

18. Automatic alarm initiating systems equipped with alarm verification features shall be permitted provided _____.

I.   actuation of an alarm initiating device other than a smoke detector shall cause a system alarm signal within 10 seconds
II. a smoke detector continuously subjected to a smoke concentration above alarm threshold magnitude initiates a system alarm within 2 minutes

(a) I only (b) II only (c) I and II (d) none of these

19. Where both coded sprinkler supervisory signals and coded fire or waterflow alarm signals are transmitted over the same circuit, provision shall be made to either obtain _____ of the fire alarm signal, to prevent the loss of an alarm signal.

I. alarm signal by-pass   II. sufficient repetition   III. alarm signal precedence

(a) I only (b) I and III (c) II and III (d) I and II

20. Connections to the light and power service shall be on a _____ branch circuit.

(a) multiple (b) dedicated (c) general purpose (d) appliance

21. Each fire alarm box shall be securely mounted. The operable part of the box shall not be less than _____ and not more than _____ above the floor level.

(a) 4' ... 5' (b) 48" ... 52" (c) 3 1/2' ... 4' (d) 4' ... 6'

22. All apparatus shall be restored to normal _____ after each test or alarm.

(a) within 30 minutes (b) within 30 seconds (c) within 2 minutes (d) as promptly as possible

23. A fire alarm system whose components might be used in whole or in part, in common with a nonfire signal system such as a paging system, a security system, a building automatic system, or a process monitoring system is a ___.

(a) primary system (b) combination system (c) low-voltage system (d) none of these

24. A switch for silencing the alarm signal sounding appliance shall be permitted only if it is _____.

I.   key operated or located within a locked cabinet
II. capable of transferring the alarm indication to a visual indicator
III. manually operated and located in an unlocked cabinet

(a) I only (b) II only (c) I and II (d) I, II and III

25. When speakers are used to produce audible fire alarm signals, which of the following shall apply?

I.   Failure of the audio amplifier shall result in an audible trouble signal.
II. Failure of the tone generating equipment shall result in an audible trouble signal.
III. Failure of the tone generating and amplifying equipment enclosed as integral parts, and serving only a single listed audible signaling appliance, shall result in an audible trouble signal.

(a) I only (b) II only (c) I and II (d) I, II and III

26. Local protective systems of the electrical type must test free of grounds.

(a) true (b) false

27. Appliances intended for use in special environments such as ___ or where subject to tampering shall be listed for the intended application.

(a) high humidity (b) low temperatures (c) hazardous locations (d) all of these

28. Unless otherwise permitted or required by 10.17.1.3 through 10.17.1.14, all means of interconnecting equipment, devices, and appliances and wiring connections shall be monitored for the integrity of the interconnecting conductors or equivalent path so that the occurrence of a single open or a single ground fault condition in the installation conductors or other signaling channels is automatically indicated within ___ seconds.

(a) 10 (b) 30 (c) 60 (d) 200

29. A pressure tank supervisory signal initiating device for a pressure tank shall detect both high and low pressure conditions. A signal shall be obtained when the pressure is increased or decreased ___ psi from the required pressure value.

(a) 10 (b) 20 (c) 25 (d) 30

30. Homeowners shall test systems in accordance with the manufacturer's instructions and shall have every residential fire alarm system tested by a qualified service technician at least every ____ years to maintain reliability.

(a) 1 (b) 2 (c) 3 (d) 5

31. Manual fire alarm boxes shall be distributed throughout the protected area so that they are unobstructed, readily accessible, and located in the normal path of exit from the area, and ____.

I.   at least one box shall be provided on every other floor
II. additional boxes shall be provided so that travel distance to the nearest box will not be in excess of 200 feet
III. at least one box shall be provided on each floor
IV. additional boxes shall be provided so that travel distance to the nearest box will not be in excess of 300 feet

(a) I and II (b) II and III (c) I and IV (d) none of these

32. The secondary power supply shall automatically supply the energy to the system within _____ seconds whenever the primary power supply is incapable.

(a) 10   (b) 15   (c) 30   (d) 60

33. When the same sound is used for both supervisory and trouble signals, distinction between signals shall be by other appropriate means such as visible annunciation.

(a) true   (b) false

34. A switch for silencing the trouble signal sounding appliance shall be permitted if it transfers the trouble indication to a lamp or other acceptable visible indicator.

(a) true   (b) false

35. Automatic alarm initiating devices which have integral trouble signal _____ shall be wired on the initiating device circuit.

(a) alarms   (b) circuits   (c) contacts   (d) wiring

36. Unless otherwise permitted or required by 10.17.1.3 through 10.17.1.14, all means of interconnecting equipment, devices, and appliances and wiring connections shall be _____ of the interconnecting conductors or equivalent path so that the occurrence of a single open or a single ground fault condition in the installation conductors or other signaling channels is automatically indicated within 200 seconds.

(a) double insulated   (b) torqued   (c) monitored for integrity   (d) meggered

37. Shunt type auxiliary systems shall be so arranged that one auxiliary transmitter does not serve more than _____ sq.ft. total area.

(a) 20,000   (b) 50,000   (c) 75,000   (d) 100,000

38. After successful completion of acceptance tests approved by the authority having jurisdiction, the owner is responsible for maintaining the records. A complete record of the tests and operations of each system shall be kept until the next test and for ___ year(s) thereafter.

(a) 1   (b) 2   (c) 3   (d) 4

39. A publicly accessible fire alarm box that can also be operated by one or more remote initiating devices or an auxiliary alarm system is a/an ____.

(a) **auxiliary alarm box**   (b) **neutral fire alarm box**
(c) **municipal fire alarm box**   (d) **master box**

40. A manually operated device used to initiate a fire alrm signal is a/an ____.

(a) **auxiliary alarm box**   (b) **neutral fire alarm box**
(c) **manual fire alarm box**   (d) **master box**

41. The NFPA standard for initiating devices for fire alarm systems is ____.

(a) **10B**   (b) **72**   (c) **12A**   (d) **70**

42. Fixed temperature detectors shall have a temperature rating of at least ___°f above the maximum expected temperature at the ceiling.

(a) **20**   (b) **30**   (c) **45**   (d) **50**

43. A complete unalterable record of the tests and operations of each system shall be kept until the next test and for ____ year(s) thereafter. The record shall be available for examination and where required, reported to the authority having jurisdiction. Archiving of records by any means shall be permitted if hard copies of the records can be provided promptly when requested.

(a) **1**   (b) **2**   (c) **3**   (d) **5**

44. No more than ____ smoke detectors may be interconnected in a multiple station connection, where the interconnecting means is not supervised.

(a) **2**   (b) **5**   (c) **10**   (d) **12**

45. Automatic fire suppression system alarm initiating devices and supervisory signal initiating devices and their circuits shall be designed and installed so that they cannot be subject to ___ without initiating a signal. .

I. tampering   II. opening   III. removal

(a) I only   (b) I and III only   (c) II and III only   (d) I, II or III

46. The spacing between detectors in irregularly shaped areas may be greater than the listed spacing, provided the farthest point of a sidewall or corner within its zone is not greater than ___ times the listed spacing.

(a) 0.6   (b) .12   (c) 1.80   (d) 0.7

47. Conductors of the shunt circuits shall not be smaller than _____ AWG and shall be insulated.

(a) #18   (b) #16   (c) #14   (d) #12

48. All communication and transmission channels between the proprietary supervising station and the protected premises control unit (panel) shall be operated manually or automatically once every ____ hours to verify operation.

(a) 24   (b) 36   (c) 48   (d) 60

49. Equipment shall be so designed that it shall be capable of performing its intended function at ____.

I.   a relative humidity of 85 and an ambient temperature of 86°
II. ambient temperatures of 32° F and 120°F
III. 85% and at 110% of the nameplate primary (main) and secondary (standby) input voltages

(a) I only   (b) II only   (c) III only   (d) I, II and III

50. A facility that receives signals from protected premises fire alarm systems and at which personnel are in attendance at all times to respond to these signals is known as a _____.

(a) supervising station   (b) subsidiary station   (c) transmission station   (d) subscriber station

51. Trouble signals shall be distinctive from alarm signals and shall be indicated by distinctive _____ except as permitted in 10.7.3..

(a) audible signals (b) relays (c) contactors (d) remote switches

52. A _____ system is a system used to connect the protected premises system to a public emergency alarm reporting system for transmitting an alarm to the communications center.

(a) remote (b) auxiliary alarm (c) shunt (d) parallel telephone

53. Leads from rectifiers or motor generators, with a float charged battery, shall be protected by fuses rated at not less than 1 amp and not more than _____ percent of maximum connected load.

(a) 100 (b) 115 (c) 125 (d) 200

54. Both sides of the auxiliary circuit shall be in the same conduit. Where a shunt loop is used, it shall not exceed a length of _____ and shall be in conduit.

(a) 100' (b) 300' (c) 500' (d) 750'

55. All apparatus shall be restored to normal _____ after each test or alarm, and kept in normal condition for operation.

(a) within 30 seconds   (b) as promptly as possible
(c) as soon as possible   (d) within 90 seconds

56. A spare DARR shall be provided in the supervising station and shall be able to be switched in place of a failed unit within _____ after detection of failure.

(a) 10 seconds (b) 15 seconds (c) 30 seconds (d) 60 seconds

57. If a regular signal is not received from a guard's tour supervisory signal within a _____ minute maximum grace period, or if a guard fails to follow a prescribed route in transmitting the signals, the proprietary supervising station operator shall initiate an action.

(a) 5 (b) 15 (c) 30 (d) 45

58. A signal initiated by a system or device indicative of a fault in a monitored circuit, system, or component is defined as ____.

(a) a trouble signal   (b) a ground-fault signal
(c) an alarm signal   (d) a supervisory signal

59. Sufficient fuel for an engine-driven generator shall be available in storage for ____ of operation at full load, unless otherwise required or permitted in 10.5.10.6.1 to 10.5.10.6.3.

(a) one year   (b) 6 months of testing plus 24 hours
(c) 6 months of testing plus 3 days   (d) 6 months of testing plus the capacity specified in 10.5.6

60. A signal indicating the need for action in connection with the supervision of guards or system attendents is a ___ signal.

(a) alarm   (b) fire alarm   (c) delinquency   (d) evacuation

61. When a remote supervising station connection is used to transmit an alarm signal, the signal shall be received at ____.

I. the fire station
II. a governmental agency that has the public responsibility for taking the prescribed action needed
III. the public fire service communication center

(a) I only   (b) II only   (c) III only   (d) I, II and III

62. The secondary power supply shall automatically provide power to the supervising station facility and equipment within ___ whenever the primary power supply fails to provide minimum voltage required for proper operation.

(a) 5 seconds   (b) 45 seconds   (c) 30 seconds   (d) 60 seconds

63. A heat sensing detector integrally mounted on a smoke detector shall be listed for not less than ____ feet of spacing.

(a) 50   (b) 40   (c) 25   (d) 10

64. The number of waterflow alarm initiating devices permitted to be connected to a single initiating device circuit shall not exceed ____.

(a) 5   (b) 12   (c) 25   (d) 50

65. Where suitable audible means is provided in the proprietary supervising station to readily identify the type of signal received, a common audible indicating appliance shall be permitted to be used for alarm, supervisory, and trouble indication.

(a) true   (b) false

66. Location designating lights of distinctive color, visible for at least ____ feet in all directions shall be installed over publicly accessible boxes.

(a) 100   (b) 500   (c) 1000   (d) 1500

67. For the purpose of alarm annunciation, each floor of the building shall be considered ___.

(a) a zone of origin   (b) a separate zone   (c) a positive alarm sequence   (d) none of these

68. A signal indicating an emergency condition or an alert requiring immediate action, such as an alarm for fire from a manual box is defined as ____ signal.

(a) a fire   (b) an alarm   (c) a trouble   (d) a warning

69. All devices, combination of devices, and equipment to be installed in a fire warning system shall be ____ for the purposes for which they are intended.

I. listed   II. approved

(a) I only   (b) II only   (c) I & II   (d) I or II

70. The signal from an automatic fire detection device selected for positive alarm sequence operation shall be acknowledged at the control unit by trained personnel within ____ seconds of annunciation in order to initiate the alarm investigation phase.

(a) 2   (b) 5   (c) 10   (d) 15

71. The circuit disconnecting means shall have a red marking and accessible only to authorized personnel and shall be clearly marked ____.

(a) remote station   (b) disconnect   (c) alarm control circuit   (d) fire alarm circuit

72. A control valve shall be supervised to obtain a distinctive signal, indicating movement of the valve from its normal position. The off-normal signal shall be obtained either during the ____ revolutions of a hand wheel or when the stem of the valve has moved one-fifth of the distance from its normal position.

(a) first two   (b) first three   (c) last two   (d) last three

73. When intermediate stations which do not transmit a signal are employed in conjunction with signal transmitting stations, distinctive signals shall be transmitted ____ of each tour of a guard.

I. at each intermediate station   II. only at the end   III. only at the beginning

(a) I and II   (b) II only   (c) II and III   (d) I and III

74. The alarm system shall either display or record alarm signals at a rate not slower than one every ____ seconds, regardless of the rate or number of status changes occurring, without loss of any signals.

(a) 10   (b) 20   (c) 60   (d) 90

75. The system shall automatically transmit a ____ signal within 15 minutes after the predetermined actuation time if a guard fails to actuate tour stations as scheduled.

(a) warning   (b) delinquency   (c) alert   (d) trouble

76. The visual representation of output data other than printed data is defined as ____.

(a) display   (b) graphic   (c) charted   (d) pictorial

77. Parts of a circuit can be intentionally and permanently grounded to provide ____.

I. noise suppression   II. ground fault detection   III. emergency ground signaling

(a) I only   (b) II only   (c) III only   (d) I, II and III

78. Exposed water storage containers exposed to freezing conditions shall be supervised to obtain two separate and distinct signals, one indicating that the temperature of the water has been lowered to 40°F and the other indicating restoration to a temperature above 40°F.

(a) true   (b) false

79. Line-type heat detectors shall be located on the ceiling or on the side walls not more than ____ from the ceiling.

(a) 12"   (b) 20"   (c) 24"   (d) 30"

80. All penetrations of a return air duct in the vicinity of detectors installed on or in an air duct shall be sealed to prevent entrance of outside air and possible ___ or redirection of smoke within the duct.

(a) evaporation   (b) increase   (c) dilution   (d) ignition

81. After installation, a visual inspection of all detectors shall be made to ensure that there are no changes that would effect ____ .

(a) equipment performance   (b) usage   (c) both a & b (d) neither a nor b

82. A means that is available only to the agency responsible for maintaining the public emergency alarm reporting system shall be provided for disconnecting the auxiliary loop to the connected property.

(a) true   (b) false

83. ____ is a body or stream of gaseous material involved in the combustion process and emitting radiant energy at specific wavelength bands determined by the combustion chemistry of the fuel.

(a) Fire   (b) Flame   (c) Smoke   (d) Heat

84. A row of detectors shall first be first located at or within ____ feet of the peak of the ceiling.

(a) 3   (b) 3 1/2   (c) 4   (d) 6

85. A ____ type detector is a device whose detecting element is concentrated at a particular location.

(a) smoke   (b) spot   (c) line   (d) air sampling

86. Records of all inspections, tests, and maintenance shall be retained until the next test and for ____ thereafter.

(a) 6 months   (b) 1 year   (c) 3 years   (d) life of the system

87. Where ceiling mounted smoke detectors are to be installed on a smooth ceiling for a single or double doorway, they shall be located ____.

I. on the centerline of the doorway
II. no more than 5' measured along the ceiling and perpendicular to the doorway

(a) I only   (b) II only   (c) both I and II   (d) neither I nor II

88. A ____ is a device that will respond when its operating element becomes heated to a predetermined level.

(a) flame detector   (b) smoke detector   (c) fixed temperature detector   (d) fire-gas detector

89. Smoke detectors shall not be installed in areas where the normal ambient temperature is likely to exceed ____ ° F or fall below 32° F unless specifically listed.

(a) 100   (b) 140   (c) 194   (d) 212

90. A rate of rise detector is a device which will respond when the temperature rises to a predetermined level.

(a) true   (b) false

91. A spacing of ____ feet may be used as a guide for spacing and locating spot-type smoke detectors on smooth ceilings, in the absence of specific performance based design criteria.

(a) 20   (b) 30   (c) 50   (d) 75

92. All metallic cables with taps and splices made shall be tested for insulation resistance when installed, but before connection to terminals. Such tests shall indicate an insulation resistance of at least ____ megohms per mile between any one conductor and all others, the sheath, and ground.

(a) 10 (b) 50 (c) 100 (d) 200

93. Air duct detectors shall be securely installed in such a way as to obtain a representative sample of airstream. This shall be permitted to be achieved by being ____.

I. rigidly mounted within the duct
II. mounted outside the duct with rigidly mounted sampling tubes protruding into the duct
III. mounted through the duct with a projected light beam

(a) I only (b) I & II only (c) II & III only (d) I & II & III

94. With certain exceptions, detectors shall be required underneath open loading docks or platforms.

(a) true (b) false

95. A line type or spot type sensing element in which resistance varies as a function of temperature is a ____ detector.

(a) electrical conductivity heat (b) fire gas (c) flame (d) none of these

96. The spacing and location of smoke detectors shall result only after careful consideration of which of the following?

I. compartment ventilation II. ceiling height III. ceiling shape

(a) I only (b) II only (c) III only (d) I, II and III

97. Open joist construction is ceilings having beams projecting below the ceiling surface more than four inches and spaced more than three feet center to center.

(a) true (b) false

98. Smoke detectors or smoke alarms listed as field adjustable shall be permitted to either be adjusted within the listed and marked sensitivity range, cleaned, and recalibrated.

(a) true (b) false

99. Where automatic testing is performed at least ____ by a remotely monitored fire alarm control unit specifically listed for this application. The manual testing frequency shall be permitted to be extended to annually.

(a) daily   (b) weekly   (c) monthly   (d) quarterly

100. To avoid nuisance alarms, the location of smoke detectors shall take into consideration potential ambient sources of ____, and electrical or mechanical influences.

I. dust   II. moisture   III. smoke   IV. fumes

(a) I only   (b) III only   (c) II, III and IV   (d) I, II, III and IV

NFPA
72

FINAL EXAM

100 QUESTIONS　　　**TIME LIMIT 5 HOURS**

1. A building that has rooms with sloped ceilings with solid joists or beams, all ceiling mounted detectors shall be located _____ of such joists or beams.

(a) in the middle   (b) beside the center   (c) on the bottom   (d) none of these

2. Prior to system maintenance or testing, the record of completion and any information required by section 10.18 regarding the system and system alterations including _____ shall be made available by the owner or designated representative to the service personnel.

I. wiring diagrams   II. floor plans   III. specifications

(a) I & II only   (b) I & III only   (c) II & III only   (d) I, II & III

3. Smoke detectors mounted in rooms with ceiling slopes greater than _____ rise per _____ horizontally shall be located within 36 inches of the high side of the ceiling but not closer than 4 inches from the adjoining wall surface.

(a) 6"...8'   (b) 1'...8'   (c) 1'...6'   (d) 6"...8"

4. Provision shall be made to indicate the flow of water in a sprinkler system by an alarm signal within _____ after flow of water equal to or greater than that from a single sprinkler of the smallest orifice size installed in the system.

(a) 30 seconds   (b) one minute   (c) 90 seconds   (d) two minutes

5. Provision shall be made to indicate the flow of water in a sprinkler system, except movement due to _____, by an alarm signal at the central station.

I. waste   II. surges   III. variable pressure

(a) I only   (b) II only   (c) III only   (d) I, II and III

6. A device that detects the radiant energy emitted by a flame is a _____ detector.

(a) flame   (b) smoke   (c) fire-gas   (d) heat

7. The detector sensitivity cannot be tested or measured using any spray device that administers an unmeasured concentration of aerosol into the detector.

(a) true   (b) false

8. In a proprietary system, when the runner is not in attendance at the proprietary supervising station, the runner shall establish two-way communications with the central station at intervals not exceeding _____ minutes.

(a) 15   (b) 20   (c) 30   (d) 45

9. Fire alarm, supervisory, and trouble signals shall be permitted to be received at the _____.

I. central station   II. communication center that meets NFPA 1221   III. police headquarters

(a) I only   (b) II only   (c) III only   (d) I, II and III

10. Shunt systems shall be _____ with respect to any remote electrical tripping or actuating devices.

(a) noncoded   (b) coded   (c) opened   (d) closed

11. A switch for silencing the audible trouble signal shall not be permitted where the visual signal remains operating until the silencing switch is restored to its normal position.

(a) true   (b) false

12. A system in which transponders are employed to transmit status signals of each initiating device circuit within a prescribed time interval is a _____.

I. dual control system   II. central station system   III. active multiplex system

(a) I only   (b) II only   (c) III only   (d) none of these

13. A household fire alarm system is a system of devices that uses a fire alarm control unit to produce an alarm signal for the purpose of notifying the occupants of the presence of a fire so that they will evacuate the premises.

(a) true   (b) false

14. A____ is a device that is intended to detect the radiant energy emitted by a flame.

(a) flame detector   (b) smoke detector   (c) heat detector   (d) fire-gas detector

15. A fixed temperature heat detector which is color coded **green** has a temperature classification of ____.

(a) 212°   (b) 450°   (c) extra high   (d) very extra high

16. The location of the equipment needed to relay signals between the protected premises, subsidiary stations and central supervising station is defined as a ____.

(a) main line facility   (b) repeater station   (c) trunk facility   (d) auxiliary facility

17. Storage batteries shall be located so that the equipment, including overcurrent devices, are not adversely affected by ____ and shall confirm to the requirements of NFPA 70.

(a) ambient temperature   (b) GFCI   (c) battery gases   (d) utility outage

18. Upon receipt of an alarm, a supervisory, or a trouble signal by the remote supervising station other than the communications center, the ____ shall be responsible for notifying the owner's designated representative immediately.

(a) runner   (b) fire station   (c) lead person   (d) operator on duty

19. An auxiliary alarm system which employs a locally complete arrangement of parts, initiating devices, relays, power supply, and associated components to automatically activate a master box or auxiliary box over circuits that are electrically isolated from the public emergency alarm reporting system circuit is a ____ alarm system.

(a) local energy auxiliary   (b) parallel telephone auxiliary
(c) shunt auxiliary   (d) municipal fire station

20. Water storage containers shall be supervised to indicate when the water temperature has been lowered to ____.

(a) 32° F   (b) 40° F   (c) 50° F   (d) 60° F

21. Additional manual fire alarm boxes shall be provided so that travel to the nearest box shall not be in excess of ____ feet.

(a) 50   (b) 100   (c) 150   (d) 200

22. A pressure tank signal initiating device shall indicate both high and low water level conditions.

(a) true   (b) false

23. High frequency energy that can be modulated by voice or signaling impulses is known as ____.

(a) leg facility   (b) station   (c) channel   (d) carrier

24. A nonrestorable initiating device is a device whose sensing element is designed to be destroyed by the process of detecting a fire may be either manually or automatically restored.

(a) true   (b) false

25. All central station signaling systems shall have a record available for examination and, if required, reported to the authority having jurisdiction.

(a) true   (b) false

26. A level ceiling is one that is actually level or that has a slope of less than or equal to 1 in 8.

(a) true   (b) false

27. A building or portion of a building in which more than ____ but not more than 12 clients receive care, maintenance, and supervision, by other than their relatives or legal guardians, for less than 24 hours per day, is classified as a Day Care Home.

(a) 1   (b) 2   (c) 3   (d) 13

28. The alarm system owner shall be responsible for maintaining site specific software records for _____ of the system for examination by the authority having jurisdiction.

(a) 5 years (b) 3 years (c) 1 year (d) life

29. Spot type smoke detectors shall be located _____.

(a) 6 feet above the floor   (b) in the center of the ceiling
(c) 18" from ceiling on wall   (d) on the ceiling or sidewall

30. Area smoke detectors within smoke compartments shall be permitted to be used to control the spread of smoke by initiating appropriate operation of ___.

I. dampers II. doors III. other equipment

(a) I only (b) II only (c) III only (d) I, II and III

31. Spot type heat detectors shall be located on the ceiling, or if on a sidewall, between the ceiling and ___ down from the ceiling to the top of the detector.

(a) 4" (b) 6" (c) 8" (d) 12"

32. When intermediate stations that do not transmit a signal are employed in conjunction with signal-transmitting stations, distinctive signals shall be transmitted at the beginning and end of each tour of a guard and a signal-transmitting station shall be provided at intervals not exceeding _____ stations.

(a) 10 (b) 12 (c) 15 (d) 20

33. A switch for silencing the alarm signal sounding appliances shall be permitted only if it is _____.

I. located within a locked cabinet II. key operated III. or arranged to provide equivalent protection

(a) I only (b) II only (c) II only (d) I, II and III

34. _____ detectors are more responsive to invisible particles produced by most flaming fires.

(a) Heat (b) Ionization (c) Smoke (d) Fire-gas

35. All points on a smooth ceiling shall have a detector within a distance equal to _____ times the selected spacing.

(a) .7   (b) .8   (c) .9   (d) 1.0

36. The supervising station shall be provided with emergency lighting that shall carry on the operation of the supervising station for a ___ hour(s) period.

(a) 4   (b) 12   (c) 26   (d) 30

37. Lead acid batteries in central station facilities shall be tested for load voltage _____.

(a) manufacturers recommendation   (b) monthly   (c) annually   (d) each 3 years

38. Household fire alarm systems shall have two independent power sources consisting of a primary source that uses commercial light and power and a secondary source that consists of a rechargeable battery.

(a) true   (b) false

39. A level ceiling has a slope of less than or equal to _____.

(a) 1 1/2" per foot or more   (b) 3 in 12   (c) 1 in 8   (d) 0" per foot

40. A coded alarm signal shall consist of not less than _____ complete rounds of the number transmitted.

(a) 2   (b) 3   (c) 4   (d) 6

41. The power for shunt-type auxiliary systems shall be derived from _____.

(a) auxiliary batteries   (b) 240v stand-by
(c) public emergency alarm reporting system   (d) gasoline driven generator

42. An automatic sequence that results in an alarm signal, even if manually delayed for investigation, unless the system is reset is defined as _____.

(a) permanent visual recording　　(b) commercial monitor
(c) positive alarm sequence　　(d) combination protective

43. Each _____ shall be programmed to call a second DACR line (number) should the signal transmission sequence to the first called line (number) be unsuccessful.

(a) DACT　(b) DACR　(c) DAAT　(d) DCAR

44. Batteries shall be protected from excessive charging current by ___.

I. overcurrent devices　II. automatic current limiting design

(a) I only　(b) II only　(c) either I or II　(d) neither I nor II

45. A signaling line circuit interface is a system component that connects a signaling line circuit to any combination of initiating devices, initiating device circuits, notification appliances and circuits, system control outputs, and other signaling line circuits

(a) true　(b) false

46. A body or stream of gaseous material involved in the combustion process and emitting radiant energy at specific wavelength bands determined by the combustion chemistry of the fuel. In most cases, some portion of the emitted radiant energy is visible to the human eye is a _____ detector.

(a) flame　(b) spark　(c) ember　(d) radiant energy

47. A electrical conductivity type detector is an example of a _____ detector.

(a) smoke　(b) photoelectric　(c) fusible alloy　(d) rate of rise

48. Manual fire alarm boxes shall be securely mounted so that the operable part of the box shall not be less than 42 inches and not more than 6' above the floor level.

(a) true　(b) false

49. A device in which detection is continuous along a path is a "line-type detector".

(a) true   (b) false

50. Initiating devices shall be supported, in all cases, independently of their attachment to the circuit conductors.

(a) true   (b) false

51. Duplicate terminals, leads, or connections that provide for the connection of installation wiring shall be provided on each initiating device for the express purpose of connecting into the fire alarm system for monitoring.

(a) true   (b) false

52. A transmitter is a system component that provides an interface between signaling line circuits, initiating device circuits, or control units and the transmission channel.

(a) true   (b) false

53. The secondary power supply capacity for supervising station facilities and equipment shall be capable of supporting operations for a minimum of ____.

(a) 30 minutes   (b) 12 hours   (c) 20 hours   (d) 24 hours

54. Changes to all control units connected or controlled by the system executive software shall require a ___ percent functional test of the system.

(a) 10   (b) 25   (c) 50   (d) 100

55. Detection is dependent upon the size and intensity of fire to provide the necessary quantity of required products and related ____ for adequate operation.

I. diffusion   II. thermal lift   III. circulation

(a) I only   (b) II only   (c) III only   (d) I, II and III

56. Manual fire alarm stations shall be used only for fire alarm initiating purposes.

(a) true   (b) false

57. A heat sensing detector integrally mounted on a smoke detector shall be listed for not less than ___ feet spacing.

(a) 20   (b) 25   (c) 35   (d) 50

58. Equipment constructed and installed in conformity with NFPA 72 shall be ____ for the purpose for which it is used.

(a) tested   (b) approved   (c) inspected   (d) listed

59. Provision shall be made to designate the building in which a signal originates. The ____ of the building shall be designated at the proprietary supervising station or at the building protected.

I. floor   II. section   III. other subdivision

(a) I only   (b) II only   (c) I & II only   (d) I, II & III

60. The ____ shall provide for proper maintenance of the system.

(a) installer   (b) property, building, or system owner   (c) maintenance employee   (d) renter

61. Manual fire alarm boxes shall be mounted on both sides of grouped openings over ____ in width, and within 60 inches of each side of the opening.

(a) 20 feet (b) 30 feet   (c) 40 feet (d) 50 feet

62. Catastrophic dry cell battery failure shall cause a trouble signal identifying the affected low power radio transmitter at its receiver/fire alarm control unit. When silenced, the trouble signal shall automatically re-sound at least once every ____ hours.

(a) 2   (b) 3   (c) 4   (d) 6

63. A _____ is a device which detects the visible or invisible particles of combustion.

(a) flame detector   (b) fire-gas detector   (c) heat detector   (d) smoke detector

64. A smoke sensing fire detector shall be spaced and located within _____ feet of the high side of a shed sloped ceiling.

(a) 3   (b) 4   (c) 4 1/2   (d) 5

65. A signal indicating the need for action in connection with the supervision of guard tours, the fire suppression systems or equipment is defined as _____ signal.

(a) a supervisory   (b) a fire   (c) an alarm   (d) a smoke

66. The secondary power supply shall automatically provide power to the supervising station facility and equipment within ___ seconds of a primary power loss.

(a) 10   (b) 20   (c) 30   (d) 60

67. Supervisory signals that latch in the off normal state and require manual reset of the system to restore them to normal shall be permitted.

(a) true   (b) false

68. Each manual fire alarm box shall be securely mounted with the operable part of the box not less than 42 inches and not more than _____ feet above the floor level.

(a) 3 1/2   (b) 4   (c) 4 1/2   (c) 6

69. All fire alarm systems shall test free of grounds.

(a) true   (b) false

70. A path for voice or signal transmission uses modulation of light or alternating current within a frequency band is defined as _____.

(a) a trouble signal   (b) a carrier   (c) a leg facility   (d) a channel

71. A system in which transponders are employed to transmit status signals of each initiating device circuit within a prescribed time interval is ____.

(a) an active multiplex system   **(b) a trunk interface system**
(c) a carrier system   **(d) a parallel telephone circuit**

72. Where required to be electronically monitored, waterflow alarm-initiating devices shall be connected to a dedicated function fire alarm control unit designated as "sprinkler waterflow and supervisory system," and permanently identified on the control unit and record drawings.

(a) true (b) false

73. Which of the following supervision circuits does **not** require two separate and distinct signals?

I.   manual alarm supervision
II. water temperature supervision
III. control valve position
IV. water level supervision

(a) I only   (b) II only   (c) III only   (d) IV only

74. Inspection, testing, or maintenance shall be permitted to be done by the building or system owner or organization other than the building or system owner if conducted under a written contract.

(a) true   (b) false

75. A coded alarm signal from a transmitter shall consist of not less than ____ complete rounds of the number transmitted.

(a) 2   (b) 3   (c) 4   (d) 6

76. Each ____ smoke detector shall be capable of initiating elevator recall when all other devices on the same initiating device circuit have been manually or automatically placed in the alarm condition.

I.   elevator machine room
II. 3rd floor elevator
III. elevator lobby

(a) III only   (b) II only   (c) II and III   (d) I and III

77. Hold up alarms or other life threatening signals shall not be permitted to take precedence over supervisory and trouble signals.

(a) **true**   (b) **false**

78. A supervisory signal initiating device for other than pressure tanks shall initiate a low water level signal when the water level falls ____ .

(a) **3"**   (b) **6"**   (c) **10"**   (d) **12"**

79. The equipment needed to relay signals between supervisory stations, subsidiary stations, and the protected premises is called a ____.

(a) **fire equipment**   (b) **repeater station**   (c) **proprietary station**   (d) **remote facility**

80. A row of detectors shall first be first located at or within ____ feet of the peak of the ceiling, measured horizontally.

(a) **18"**   (b) **2'**   (c) **3'**   (d) **30"**

81. Ceiling construction in which joists are ____ or less in depth shall be considered equivalent to a smooth ceiling.

(a) **2"**   (b) **4"**   (c) **6"**   (d) **8"**

82. A complete record of the tests and operation of each system shall be kept until the next test and for ___ thereafter.

(a) **6 months**   (b) **2 years**   (c) **1 year**   (d) **5 years**

83. That portion of a communication channel that connects not more than one protected premises to a primary or secondary trunk facility is called a ____.

(a) **trunk carrier**   (b) **trouble signal**   (c) **leg facility**   (d) **channel**

84. In the event of the failure of equipment at the subsidiary station or the communication channel to the central station, a back up shall be operational within ___.

(a) 30 seconds   (b) 60 seconds   (c) 90 seconds   (d) 4 hours

85. Appliances intended for use ___ or where subject to tampering shall be listed for the intended application.

I. outdoors   II. high temperature   III. dusty conditions

(a) I and II   (b) II and III   (c) I and III   (d) I, II and III

86. Manual fire alarm boxes shall be inspected ____.

(a) each 12 hours   (b) bimonthly   (c) semi-annually   (d) annually

87. At least one manual fire alarm box shall be provided on each floor. Additional manual fire alarm boxes shall be provided so that travel distance to the nearest fire alarm box will not be in excess of ____ feet measured horizontally on the same floor.

(a) 50   (b) 200   (c) 150   (d) none of these

88. Visible notification appliances located within 24" of the ceiling over the bed and within ___ feet of a sleeping occupant shall have a light output rating of at least 177 cd.

(a) 8   (b) 12   (c) 15   (d) 16

89. A facility that receives signals from protected premises fire alarm systems and at which personnel are in attendance at all times is defined as a fire station.

(a) true   (b) false

90. The phenomenon where the upward movement of smoke and gases ceases due to the loss of buoyancy is ___.

(a) lighter than air   (b) antilift   (c) float   (d) stratification

91. A finish signal shall be transmitted within a predetermined interval after the guard completes the last tour of the premises.

(a) true   (b) false

92. Liquid expansion and fusible alloy is a type of ____ detector.

(a) heat   (b) smoke   (c) fixed temperature   (d) rate-of-rise

93. Manual fire alarm boxes shall be used only for fire alarm initiating purposes. However, combination manual fire alarm boxes and guard's signaling stations shall be permitted.

(a) true   (b) false

94. Testing with ___ or listed aerosol approved by the manufacturer shall be permitted as acceptable test method for systems detectors.

(a) oxygen   (b) halogen   (c) smoke   (d) zinc

95. A parallel telephone system is a telephone system in which an individually wired circuit is used for each box.

(a) true   (b) false

96. Individuals who conduct a visual examination of a system or portion thereof to verify that it appears to be operating condition, in proper location, and is free of physical damage or conditions that impair operation is defined as ____ personnel.

(a) inspection   (b) service   (c) testing   (d) none of these

97. Which of the following is an example of a smoke sensing fire detector ?

I. cloud chamber   II. photoelectric   III. ionization

(a) I only   (b) II only   (c) III only   (d) I, II and III

98. Household fire warning equipment shall be permitted to be powered by a battery, provided that the battery is monitored to ensure that the _____ of the following conditions are met.

I.   All power requirements are met for at least 1 year's life, including weekly testing
II. The audible trouble signal is produced at least once every minute for 7 consecutive days
III. A readily noticeable visible indication shall be displayed when a primary battery is installed in the unit

(a) I and II only   (b) I and III only   (c) II and III only   (d) I, II and III

99. Equipment constructed and installed in conformity with NFPA 72 need not be listed for the purpose for which it is used.

(a) true   (b) false

100. The means for identifying listed equipment may vary for each organization concerned with product evaluation; some organizations do not recognize equipment as listed unless it is also labeled.

(a) true   (b) false

NFPA 75

PROTECTION OF INFORMATION
TECHNOLOGY EQUIPMENT

NFPA 75 QUESTIONS

1. In installations where inside hose is provided, the hose shall be ___ rubber lined hose with shut-off and combination solid-stream and water-spray nozzles.

(a) 1" (b) 1 1/4" (c) 1 1/2" (d) 2"

2. Listed extinguishers in information technology equipment rooms for use on fires in ordinary combustible materials shall have a minimum rating of class ____.

(a) 2A (b) 2B (c) 5A (d) 10B

3. Automatic detection systems shall be installed ____ .

I.   at the ceiling level throughout the information technology equipment area.
II. below the raised floor of the information technology equipment area containing cables.
III. above the suspended ceiling and below the raised floor in the information technology equipment room where these spaces are used to recirculate air to other parts of the building.

(a) I only (b) II only (c) I & II only (d) I, II and III

4. Sprinkler systems protecting information technology equipment rooms shall be _____ separately from other sprinkler systems.

(a) installed (b) routed (c) valved (d) sized

5. Approved flexible cord and plug assemblies used for connecting information technology equipment to the branch circuit to facilitate interchange shall not exceed ____ feet in length.

(a) 6' (b) 8' (c) 12' (d) 15'

6. Decking for raised floors in information technology equipment rooms of pressure impregnated, fire retardant treated lumber, shall have a flame spread index rating of ___ or less in accordance with NFPA 255.

(a) 15 (b) 25 (c) 50 (d) 100

7. Dampers in HVAC systems serving information technology equipment rooms shall operate upon ____.

(a) **activation on a dedicated pilot light**   (b) **activation of any alarm**
(c) **activation of the alarm bell**   (d) **activation of the smoke detectors**

8. A disconnecting means shall be provided to disconnect all ____ in data processing rooms.

I. electronic equipment   II. HVAC systems   III. close all required fire/smoke dampers

(a) **I & III only**   (b) **I & III only**   (c) **II & III only**   (d) **I, II & III**

9. ____ is/are permitted as the wiring method for the branch circuit supplying receptacles or field-wired equipment under the raised floor in data processing rooms.

(a) **Rigid nonmetallic conduit**   (b) **Flexible metal conduit**   (c) **AC cable**   (d) **All of these**

10. The branch circuit conductors supplying data processing systems, shall have an ampacity of not less than ____ percent of the total connected load.

(a) **100**   (b) **110**   (c) **125**   (d) **150**

11. Air ducts serving other rooms shall be permitted to pass through computer rooms provided ____.

(a) **the area above the suspended ceiling is used as a return air**
(b) **only one register is installed to serve the computer room**
(c) **only two registers are installed to serve the computer room**
(d) **fire dampers are installed in the ducts**

12. Vital or important records that have not been duplicated shall be stored in listed record protection equipment with a Class ____ one-hour or better fire resistance rating.

(a) **100**   (b) **110**   (c) **150**   (d) **none of these**

13. Emergency and recovery procedures shall include a management approved written and dated and semi-annually tested emergency fire plan.

(a) true   (b) false

14. Power cables, communications cables, connecting cables, interconnecting cables, and associated boxes, connectors, plugs, and receptacles that are listed as part of, or for, information technology equipment shall be secured in place by _____.

(a) staples   (b) straps   (c) approved clamps   (d) are not required to be secured

15. Each unit of an information technology system supplied by a branch circuit shall be provided with a manufacturer's nameplate, which shall also include the input power requirements for _____.

I. voltage   II. frequency   III. maximum rated load in volt-amps

(a) I only   (b) II only   (c) I & II only   (d) I, II & III

NFPA 780

INSTALLATION OF LIGHTNING PROTECTION SYSTEMS

1. Gently sloping roofs are defined as _____.

(a) **a span of 40 feet or less and a pitch of 1/8 inch or less**
(b) **a span of 30 feet or less and a pitch of 1/8 inch or less**
(c) **a span of 60 feet and a pitch of less than 1/4 inch**
(d) **a span of 40 feet or less and a pitch of less than 1/8 inch**

2. The zone of protection includes the space not intruded by a rolling sphere having a radius of _____ feet.

(a) **150** (b) **125** (c) **100** (d) **50**

3. For structures with multiple level roofs no more than 50 feet in height, the zone of protection forms a cone having an apex at the highest point of the air terminal, with walls forming approximately a 45 or ___ degree angle from vertical.

(a) **50** (b) **63** (c) **90** (d) **95**

4. The tip of an air terminal shall be not less than _____ above the object or area it is to protect.

(a) **2 feet** (b) **18 inches** (c) **10 inches** (d) **6 inches**

5. Lightning protection copper components shall be protected from corrosion within _____ of the top of a chimney or vent emitting corrosive gases by a hot dipped lead coating or equivalent.

(a) **6"** (b) **12"** (c) **18"** (d) **24"**

6. Class I materials are used for the protection of structures not exceeding _____ feet.

(a) **25** (b) **75** (c) **100** (d) **150**

7. A _____ is a strike termination device that is a receptor for attachment of flashes to the lightning protection system.

(a) **air terminal** (b) **ground terminal** (c) **surge arrester** (d) **bond**

8. Each radial electrode shall be not less than ___ in length and not less than 18" below grade and shall diverge at an angle not greater than 90 degrees.

(a) 12' (b) 18' (c) 24' (d) 30'

9. The ground rods shall extend vertically not less than ____ feet into the earth.

(a) 8 (b) 10 (c) 12 (d) 20

10. Ground rods shall be copper-clad steel, solid copper, hot dipped galvanized steel, or stainless steel, but research has been presented that warns that ____ is very susceptible to corrosion in many soil conditions.

(a) stainless steel (b) galvanized steel (c) solid copper (d) copper-clad steel

11. The down conductor shall be protected from physical damage for a minimum distance of ____ above grade level.

(a) 3 feet (b) 4 feet (c) 6 feet (d) entire length

12. Ground rods shall be no less than ____ inches in diameter and ____ feet in length.

(a) 5/8...8 (b) 5/8...10 (c) 1/2...8 (d) 1/2...10

13. Structures exceeding ____ feet in perimeter shall have a down conductor for every ____ feet of perimeter .

(a) 100...50 (b) 150...50 (c) 200...100 (d) 250...100

14. A roof 90 feet in width will require ____ cross runs.

(a) 1 (b) 2 (c) 3 (d) 5

15. Air terminals on a lower roof level that are interconnected by a conductor run from a higher roof level only require one horizontal or downward path to ground provided the lower level roof conductor run does not exceed ____ feet.

(a) 25 (b) 40 (c) 50 (d) 75

16. A/an _____ shall be permitted as strike termination devices on watercraft provided they meet the requirements of 10.3.2.1.

(a) masts (b) handrails (c) both a & b (d) neither a (or) b

17. It has been shown that in cases where damage has occurred to a protected structure, the damage was due to additions or repairs to the building or to deterioration or mechanical damage that was allowed to go undetected and unrepaired, or both. Therefore, it is recommended that an annual visual inspection be made and that the system be thoroughly inspected every ___ years.

(a) 2 (b) 3 (c) 4 (d) 5

18. All grounded media and buried metallic conductors in and on a structure shall be connected to the lightning protection system within _____ feet of the base of the structure.

(a) 2 (b) 6 (c) 12 (d) 20

19. The interconnection of the lightning protection system down conductors and other grounded media at the intermediate levels between the roof and the base of a structure is known as _____.

(a) bonding potential   **(b) grounding potential**
(c) final level potential equalization   **(d) intermediate level potential equalization**

20. A bonding connection is required when the total of the _____ between the lightning conductor and the isolated metal body and the shortest distance between the isolated metal body and the grounded metal body is equal to or less than the bonding distance as calculated.

(a) shortest distance   **(b) longest distance**
(c) average of longest and shortest   **(d) total of longest and shortest**

21. The structural steel framework of a structure may be utilized as the main _____ of a lightning protection system.

(a) conductor (b) air gap (c) air terminal (d) none of these are correct

22. Lightning protection roof conductors or other concealed horizontal conductor runs shall be connected to the reinforcing steel at intervals not exceeding _____ feet.

(a) 12 (b) 25 (c) 75 (d) 100

23. At least _____ down conductors shall be provided for the tower of a wind turbine.

(a) two (b) three (c) four (d) five

24. All railroad tracks that are located within _____ feet of an explosives facility shall be bonded to the lightning protection system ground ring electrode.

(a) 6 (b) 8 (c) 10 (d) 12

25. Grounding electrodes shall be connected to steel columns around the perimeter of a structure at intervals averaging not more than _____ feet.

(a) 30 (b) 40 (c) 50 (d) 60

NFPA 101

LIFE SAFETY

NFPA 101 LIFE SAFETY QUESTIONS

1. The purpose of this Code is to establish minimum requirements, with due regard to function, ____ and maintenance of buildings and structures for safety to life from fire and similar emergencies.

I. for the design   II. operation

(a) **I only** (b) **II only** (c) **I or II** (d) **I and II**

2. A professional engineer is a person registered or licensed to practice engineering in a jurisdiction, subject to all laws and limitations imposed by the jurisdiction.

(a) **true**   (b) **false**

3. Buildings or portions of buildings shall be permitted to be occupied during construction, repair, alterations, or additions only if all ____ are in place and continuously maintained for the portion occupied.

I. means of egress   II. fire protection features

(a) **I only** (b) **II only** (c) **I & II** (d) **none of these**

4. A/an ____ is a floor opening or series of floor openings connecting two or more stories that are covered at the top of the series of openings and are used for purposes other than an enclosed stairway, elevator hoistway, escalator opening or utility shaft.

(a) **ventilation duct** (b) **atrium** (c) **draft stop** (d) **material chute**

5. That portion of exit access that must be traversed before two separate and distinct paths of travel to two exits are available is known as ____.

(a) **street floor** (b) **common path of travel** (c) **one path of travel** (d) **all of these**

6. A space, in a path of travel leading to a public way, that is protected from the effects of fire, either by means of separation from other spaces in the same building or by virtue of location, thereby permitting a delay in egress travel from any level is known as ____.

(a) **area of refuge** (b) **exit discharge** (c) **exit access corridor** (d) **ramp**

7. Fire barriers separating buildings or areas between which there are horizontal exits shall have a minimum _____ fire resistance rating, unless otherwise provided in 7.2.4.4.1.

(a) **15 minute** (b) **30 minute** (c) **1 hour** (d) **2 hour**

8. Changes in level in means of egress shall be by a ramp or a stair where the elevation difference is more than _____.

(a) **30"** (b) **21"** (c) **18"** (d) **10"**

9. An existing stairway shall have a minimum head room of _____ .

(a) **6' 4"** (b) **6'6"** (c) **6'8"** (d) **7'**

10. Exit access doors serving a room not larger than _____ sq. ft. and not required to be accessible to persons in wheelchairs shall not be less than _____ inches in door width.

(a) **50...32** (b) **50...24** (c) **70...32** (d) **70...24**

11. The elevation of the floor surfaces on both sides of a door shall not vary by more than _____ inch.

(a) **1/4** (b) **1/2** (c) **3/4** (d) **1**

12. Door openings in means of eqress shall be at least ___ in clear width.

(a) **48** (b) **36** (c) **32** (d) **30**

13. Panic hardware, when required to be used, shall cause the door latch to release when a force of not to exceed _____ lbf is applied to the releasing devices in the direction of travel.

(a) **15** (b) **18** (c) **21** (d) **none of these**

14. Any device or _____ installed to restrict the improper use of a means of egress shall be designed and installed so that it cannot, even in case of failure, impede or prevent emergency use of such means of egress.

(a) **lock** (b) **automatic release** (c) **restriction** (d) **alarm**

15. Where revolving doors are permitted as a component in a means of egress ____.

I. each revolving door shall be credited with no more than 50 persons capacity
II. each revolving door shall not be given credit for more than 50 percent of the required egress capacity
III. each revolving door shall be capable of being collapsed in a book-fold capacity

(a) I only (b) II only (c) I & II only (d) I, II & III

16. Turnstiles at a means of egress and credited for 50 persons capacity shall not be over ____ inches high nor have a clear width less than 16 1/2 inches.

(a) 39 (b) 36 (c) 32 (d) 30

17. The maximum height of risers for an existing stairway is ____.

(a) 6" (b) 7" (c) 7 1/2" (d) 8"

18. Where specifically permitted for individual occupancies, a spiral stair shall be permitted as a component in a means of egress provided ____.

I. all treads are identical
II. headroom shall not be less than 7'6"
III. the occupant load served shall not exceed 5
IV. the clear width of the stairs shall not be less than 26"

(a) I & II only (b) I, III & IV only (c) II and IV only (d) I, II, III & IV

19. Means of egress such as stairs, landings, balconies, corridors, passageways, floor or roof openings, ramps, aisles, porches, or mezzanines that are more than ____ above the floor or grade below shall be provided with guards to prevent falls over the open side.

(a) 24" (b) 30" (c) 36" (d) 40"

20. The travel distance to an exit shall be measured on the floor or other walking surface, along the center line of the natural path of travel, starting from the ____ subject to occupancy.

(a) most remote point (b) rear corner of the room (c) next means of egress (d) all of these

21. Where any part of an exterior exit is within ____ feet horizontal distance of any unprotected building opening, as permitted by the exceptions for outside stairs, the travel distance to the exit shall include the length of travel to ground level.

(a) 1 (b) 5 (c) 7 1/2 (d) 10

22. Areas accessible to people with severe mobility impairment, other than in existing buildings, shall have a minimum of ____ accessible means of egress, unless otherwise provided in 7.5.4.1.2 through 7.5.4.1.4.

(a) 1 (b) 2 (c) 4 (d) 5

23. Illumination of means of egress shall be from a source ___, such as public utility electric service.

(a) considered reliable (b) uninterruptible (c) guaranteed (d) UPS

24. Where emergency lighting maintenance of illumination depends on changing from one energy source to another, a delay of not more than ___ seconds shall be permitted.

(a) 15 (b) 12 (c) 10 (d) 5

25. In the event of any interruption of normal lighting, such as ____, the emergency lighting system shall be arranged to provide the required illumination automatically.

I. power failure of public utilities or other outside electrical power II. opening of a circuit breaker

(a) I and II (b) I only (c) II only (d) none of these

26. No ____ electric light nor any type of portable lamp or lantern shall be used for primary illumination of means of egress.

(a) D.C. powered (b) A.C /D.C. powered (c) battery operated (d) dual battery operated

27. Emergency illumination shall be provided for a period of ____ hours in the event of failure of normal lighting.

(a) 1 (b) 1 1/2 (c) 2 (d) 2 1/2

28. Where the total area of all the rehibilitation work areas included in a modification exceeds ___ percent of the area of the building, the work shall be considered as a reconstruciton and shall comply with the requirements.

(a) 25 (b) 50 (c) 60 (d) 75

29. Externally illuminated signs shall be illuminated by not less than ____ foot candles at the illuminated surface and shall have a contrast ratio of not less than 0.5.

(a) 5 (b) 7 1/2 (c) 10 (d) 20

30. For exit doors, the sign shall be mounted on the door or adjacent to the door, with the nearest edge of the sign within ___ inches of the door frame.

(a) 12 (b) 24 (c) 48 (d) 4

31. New sign placement shall be such that no point in an exit access corridor is in access of the rated viewing distance or ____ feet, whichever is less, from the nearest sign.

(a) 25 (b) 50 (c) 100 (d) no limit

32. A maximum travel distance of ____ feet to an exit is required in high hazard occupancies.

(a) 75 (b) 110 (c) 125 (d) 150

33. Fire window assemblies shall be permitted in fire barriers having a required fire resistance rating of ____ or less and shall be of an approved type with appropriate fire protection rating for the location in which the barriers are installed.

(a) 1/2 hour (b) 1 hour (c) 1 1/2 hours (d) 2 hours

34. When a conduit or duct passes through a fire barrier and transmission of vibration must be considered, vibration isolation shall be made ____.

(a) on the outside of the fire barrier   (b) on the inside of the fire barrier
(c) on either side of the fire barrier   (d) none of these are acceptable

35. For an existing alarm system, the manual fire alarm box either shall be provided in the ____ near each required exit or within 60 inches of exit doorways.

(a) natural exit access path (b) required path (c) majority egress (d) door frame

36. Where a sprinkler system provides automatic detection and alarm system initiation, it shall be provided with an approved, alarm initiation device that will operate when the flow of water is ____ that from a single automatic sprinkler.

(a) less than (b) greater than (c) equal to or greater than (d) all of these

37. For alarm annunciation, each floor of the building shall be considered as not less than ____.

(a) 1 zone (b) 2 zones (c) 4 zones (d) 6 zones

38. For alarm annunciation, if a floor exceeds ____ sq. ft. additional zoning shall be provided.

(a) 5,000 (b) 10,000 (c) 15,000 (d) 22,500

39. Seats in assembly occupancies accommodating more than ___ persons shall be securely fastened to the floor except where fastened together in groups of not less than three and as permitted by 12.7.9.1.2 and 12.7.9.2.

(a) 50 (b) 100 (c) 200 (d) 1000

40. In theaters and other assembly occupancies where persons are admitted to the building at times when seats are not available, exits shall be provided for such waiting spaces on the basis of one person for each ____ of waiting space area.

(a) 50 sq. ft. (b) 10 sq. ft. (c) 5 sq. ft. (d) 3 sq. ft.

41. The occupant load for an assembly area without fixed seats such as a dance hall shall be permitted to be based on one person per ____ net sq. ft.

(a) 7 (b) 5 (c) 3 (d) 2

42. Any door in a required means of egress from an area having an occupant load of ____ or more persons shall be permitted to be provided with a latch or lock only if it is panic hardware or fire exit hardware.

(a) 50 (b) 75 (c) 80 (d) 100

43. In assembly occupancies where there is no well defined main entrance/exit, exits shall be permitted to be distributed around the perimeter of the building, provided that the total exit width furnishes not less than ____ of the width needed to accommodate the permitted occupant load.

(a) 50% (b) 75% (c) 100% (d) 110%

44. Exits shall be arranged so that the total length of travel from any point to reach an exit shall not exceed ____ feet in any assembly occupancy.

(a) 75 (b) 100 (c) 150 (d) 200

45. In a new school, every room that is normally subject to student occupancy shall have ___ exit access door leading directly to an exit access corridor or exit.

(a) one (b) two (c) one and a window (d) two and a window

46. In an existing educational occupancy equipped with automatic sprinklers, the travel distance to an exit shall not exceed ___ ft. from any point in the building.

(a) 50 (b) 75 (c) 100 (d) 200

47. Emergency power shall be provided for all electrically power-operated sliding doors and power-operated locks. Power shall be arranged to automatically operate within ____ upon failure of normal power and to maintain the necessary power source for a minimum of 1 1/2 hours.

(a) 1 minute (b) 2 minutes (c) 5 seconds (d) 10 seconds

48. In new apartment buildings, protected throughout by an approved, supervised automatic sprinkler system, exit enclosures shall have a fire resistance rating of not less than ____ , with doors having a fire protection rating of not less than 1 hour.

(a) 1/2 hour (b) 1 hour (c) 1 1/2 hours (d) 2 hours

49. All storage occupancies shall have emergency lighting except structures____.

I. occupied only during daylight hours with skylights or windows arranged to provide the required level of illumination of all portions of means of egress
II. not normally occupied
III. with one means of egress that is sufficiently lighted

(a) I only (b) II only (c) II and III only (d) I, II, or III

50. At least one fire drill shall be conducted every ___ the educational facility is in session.

(a) day (b) week (c) month (d) year

UL 681 & 365

EXAM

80 QUESTIONS   **TIME LIMIT 4 HOURS**

80 QUESTIONS   TIME LIMIT 4 HOURS

1. Interconnecting wiring shall not be smaller than # _____ AWG copper wire and shall comply with the applicable requirements for burglar alarm wire.

(a) 16   (b) 18   (c) 20   (d) 22

2. Burglar alarm systems are categorized as _____ according to the type or principle of operation.

I. central station   II. bank   III. mercantile   IV. proprietary

(a) I or IV   (b) I, II or IV   (c) I, II or III   (d) I, II, III or IV

3. If the voltage potential is 120 across the capacitance prior to discharge, the maximum acceptable capacitance is _____ microfarads.

(a) 43.8   (b) 36.5   (c) 26.6   (d) 20.5

4. Foil on ordinary window glass shall be applied to the sides and across the bottom of each section of glass, and spaced _____ inches from the edge of the glass.

(a) 1 to 3   (b) 1 to 4   (c) 2 to 3   (d) 2 to 4

5. A tamper switch provided as part of an intrusion detection unit shall be connected in the protection circuit.

(a) true   (b) false

6. A component used in a burglar alarm system shall comply with the requirements for that component and shall not be modified _____ installation into the system.

I. after   II. during   III. before

(a) I only   (b) II only   (c) III only   (d) I, II and III

7. The alarm sounding device mounting within its intended housing and in its intended mounting position, shall provide a sound output equivalent to that of an omnidirectional source with an A-weighted sound pressure level of at least ____ decibels at ____ feet while connected to a source of rated voltage for a bank safe and vault alarm system.

(a) 97...12 (b) 87...10 (c) 87...12 (d) 110...12

8. Required protection for a safe shall be arranged so that an alarm will be initiated if an opening ____ inches or larger is made.

(a) 4 (b) 6 (c) 10 (d) 12

9. Small louvered registers may be protected by ____ if it is necessary to remove the entire register to create a manhole size opening.

I. plywood II. contacts III. traps

(a) I only (b) I and II (c) II and III (d) I, II and III

10. Of the following, ____ are acceptable sources of electrical power for grade AA police station connected burglar alarm units.

I.   rechargeable (secondary) batteries on full float or trickle charge
II. a power supply with battery standby
III. non rechargeable (primary) batteries

(a) I only (b) I & III only (c) III only (d) I, II, or III

11. The operation of a police station connected alarm system is partially under the control and domination of the owner or others interested in the property. However, it is required that police station connected systems be maintained under the care and regular inspection service of ____.

**(a) the owner   (b) any licensed installer
(c) the police department   (d) the installing company**

12. Each terminal provided for the connection of an external antenna shall be conductivity connected to the supply circuit ____ conductor.

(a) grounded (b) ungrounded (c) grounding (d) none of these

13. A mercantile premises alarm system shall be inspected at intervals sufficiently frequent to provide continuous service. The interval between regular maintenance inspections shall not exceed _____.

(a) 6 months (b) 1 year (c) 2 years (d) 5 years

14. For police station connected burglar alarm units, stranded conductors clamped under wire-binding screws or similar parts shall have _____.

(a) strands soldered individually or equivalently arranged
(b) individual strands soldered together or equivalently arranged
(c) both of these are acceptable
(d) neither of these are acceptable

15. For an Extent Number 3 system a movable window fronting and within ___ feet of a public street or highway and between 14 and 18 feet above ground and not otherwise accessible, need only be provided with partial protection.

(a) 12 (b) 25 (c) 50 (d) 75

16. Foil used on a glass surface shall be not more than _____ inch wide.

(a) 1/4 (b) 1/2 (c) 3/4 (d) 1

17. A photoelectric unit used for channel type protection shall be installed so that the beam is not less than _____ inches nor more than _____ inches from the floor.

(a) 18 ... 36 (b) 18 ... 24 (c) 36 ... 48 (d) 24 ... 36

18. When under test, the strain relief means provided on a flexible cord shall withstand for 1 minute without displacement, a pull of _____ pounds-force applied to the cord.

(a) 10 (b) 25 (c) 35 (d) 40

19. The sounding of the protected premises audible alarm may be delayed by not more than _____ minutes, but the transmission of an alarm to the police station or central station shall be delayed not more than _____ seconds for a mercantile premises alarm system.

(a) 5...45 (b) 5...50 (c) 10...15 (d) 10...20

20. Number 6 size, 1-1/2 volt non rechargeable primary ignition type cell with a drain in milliamperes of 6 and a final working voltage of 1.0, will require replacement each ____, if used on a grade A or B bank safe alarm system.

(a) 12 months (b) 10 months (c) 7 months (d) 6 months

21. A bank vault alarm shall have a standby power supply in the event of commercial power loss so that the product will be maintained in the intended condition for a period of ____ hours.

(a) 4 (b) 8 (c) 48 (d) 72

22. Any point on a building up to ___ feet from a public street or highway, that can be seen by an observer is considered "visible from the public street or highway".

(a) 100 (b) 200 (c) 300 (d) 400

23. A wire secured to a terminal with ____ does not require soldering.

I. torque II. washers III. upturned lugs

(a) I and II (b) II and III (c) I and III (d) III only

24. The minimum thickness of metal at at threaded conduit hole in a die-cast enclosure box is ___.

(a) 1/8" (b) 1/4" (c) 3/8" (d) .50

25. The area covered by a single sound detector shall not exceed ____ .

(a) 1000 sq. ft. (b) 1500 sq. ft. (c) 2000 sq. ft. (d) none of these

26. A fully framed, heat-treated or tempered glass door may be protected by ____.

I. contacts II. a closed circuit loop of foil across the top of the glass

(a) I only (b) II only (c) both I and II (d) neither I nor II

27. For extent # _____ installations, an unperforated access door on a metal duct may be protected by contacts only if the door is of the same material as the duct.

(a) one   (b) two   (c) three   (d) four

28. Of the following, _____ insulation is suitable for wiring between electrical component enclosures for a group A police station connected alarm system.

(a) XHHW   (b) SJO   (c) ST   (d) SPT-3

29. A _____ is a conductor fastened between a building structure and a screen, stripping, foiled or wired panel, fan, or similar device so that the two cannot be separated without initiating the alarm.

(a) contact   (b) semi-conductor   (c) trap   (d) pigtail

30. Fine wire directly applied to a wood door or similar surface that is in good condition and in a dry location shall be stapled at intervals not exceeding _____ inches.

(a) 8   (b) 12   (c) 18   (d) 24

31. Police station connected burglar alarm units shall not false alarm and shall operate as intended when subjected to an alternating current induced in _____ or in any other leads which extend throughout the premises wiring.

I. signal leads   II. initiating device leads   III. loops   IV. DC power leads

(a) I only   (b) I & II only   (c) II, III, & IV only   (d) I, II, III, & IV

32. Each lead employed for field connections shall withstand for one minute a pull of _____ pounds - force without evidence of damage or of transmittal of stress to the internal connections.

(a) 2   (b) 5   (c) 10   (d) 12

33. Foil on plate glass show windows shall be spaced not less than _____ inches nor more than _____ inches from the edges of the glass.

(a) 2 ... 4   (b) 3 ... 6   (c) 3 ... 5   (d) 4 ... 6

34. Each subscriber's premises shall have at least one code transmitter. Not more than _____ code transmitters may be connected in any one station circuit, and each transmitter shall give an individual distinct signal readily distinguishable as coming from that circuit rather than from any other such circuit in the police station or central station.

(a) 10 (b) 20 (c) 25 (d) 50

35. Grooved stripping used over an opening shall be secured to cross pieces that are spaced no more than ___ inches apart.

(a) 6 (b) 12 (c) 18 (d) 24

36. Iron and steel parts, other than bearings, and the like, where such protection is impracticable, shall be protected against corrosion by _____.

I. plating II. galvanizing III. enameling

(a) I only (b) II only (c) III only (d) I, II and III

37. If two or more conductors are intended to be connected by wrapping under the same screw, a _____ shall be employed for each additional conductor.

(a) ferrous intervening washer   (b) nonferrous intervening metal washer
(c) nonferrous washer   (d) none of these

38. Foil shall extend across the bottom and up the sides of each section of the show window to a height of not less than _____ feet from grade level or within _____ inches of the top of the show window.

(a) 6 ... 3 (b) 4 ... 8 (c) 3 ...7 (d) 7 ... 3

39. The audible signal at the police station or central station may be common to as many as _____ separately protected premises, but the visual signal shall be individual to each premises and shall be clearly marked.

(a) 100 (b) 75 (c) 40 (d) 10

40. For connection of other than power supply (line voltage) circuits using _____ AWG and smaller wires, a wire binding screw shall not be smaller than # 8.

(a) #22 (b) #18 (c) #12 (d) #10

41. Type _____ are permitted for connection of a portable or stationary police station connected alarm systems.

(a) SV (b) SVTO (c) SJT (d) SVT

42. A nonferrous push-in terminal of the type employed on some switches and receptacles. _____ conductors are permitted to be pushed into the slots.

I. Solid II. Aluminum III. Stranded IV. Copper

(a) IV only (b) III only (c) I and IV (d) I, II and IV

43. An enclosure shall have means for mounting which shall be _____ without disassembly of any operating part of the product.

(a) readily accessible (b) listed (c) installed (d) accessible

44. A low-voltage circuit has a potential of not more than _____ volts DC.

(a) 12 (b) 24 (c) 42.4 (d) 50

45. An opening facing an adjacent building wall without openings where the walls are spaced not more than _____ apart does not require protection.

(a) 6" (b) 12" (c) 18" (d) 24"

46. Protection of a vault should consist of _____.

I. sound and vibration detectors II. foil linings III. embedded cable

(a) I only (b) II only (c) III only (d) I, II and III

47. A control unit that has a field programmable alarm sounding circuit shall be programmed to activate the sounding device of a mercantile alarm system at normal power for not less than ___ minutes upon alarm.

(a) 15 (b) 30 (c) 45 (d) 60

48. Open wiring shall be arranged ___ with the distance between conductors not greater than 4 inches.

(a) single circuit (b) double circuit (c) by-passed (d) shunted

49. A removable screen shall be mounted so that an alarm will result if any portion of the screen frame is moved more than ____.

(a) 1/2" (b) 1" (c) 1 1/2" (d) 2"

50. Which extent may require complete protection of all accessible openings?

I. #1   II. #2   III. #3

(a) I only (b) II only (c) III only (d) I, II and III

51. Openings in the enclosure shall not give access to ____ that might be subject to tampering by hand or with tools without causing an alarm or trouble signal.

I. relays II. terminals III. controls IV. related components

(a) I only (b) II only (c) both I and II only   (d) I, II, III & IV

52. Uninsulated metal parts, such as cabinets, electrical enclosures, capacitors, and other electrical components, shall be bonded for grounding if they may be contacted by the operator or service person. Of the following, ____ need not be grounded.

I.   Panels and covers that are insulated from electrical components and wiring by an insulating barrier of vulcanized fiber, varnished cloth, phenolic composition, or similar materials not less than 0.028 inch thick, and secured in place.
II. Cabinets, panels, and covers that do not enclose uninsulated live parts if wiring is physically separated from the cabinet, panel, or cover so that they are not likely to become energized.
III. Adhesive attached metal foil markings, screws, handles, and the like, that are located on the outside of enclosures or cabinets and isolated from electrical components or wiring by grounded metal parts so that they are not likely to become energized.

(a) I, II, and III (b) II and III only (c) I and III only (d) III only

53. Interconnecting wiring between a battery or power supply and a sounding device shall not be smaller than # ___ AWG if the wire length is more than 60 feet.

(a) 18 (b) 16 (c) 22 (d) 24

54. Foil used on a wall, ceiling, floor, or door shall not be less than 3/8" nor more than 1" wide and not more than ____ " thick.

(a) .001 (b) .003 (c) .005 (d) .008

55. A flexible cord shall be of type SJ, SJT or equivalent and shall not be smaller than # ____ AWG.

(a) 18 (b) 16 (c) 14 (d) 12

56. Uninsulated high voltage live parts shall be ____.

I. located II. guarded III. enclosed

(a) I only (b) II only (c) III only (d) I, II and III

57. An electrical component that may require examination, replacement, adjustment, servicing, or maintenance while energized, shall be located with respect to grounded metal. Of the following ____ are not considered to be uninsulated live parts.

I. Coils, relays, solenoids, and transformer windings, with insulating overwraps rated for the potentials encountered.
II. Terminals and splices with insulation rated for the potential encountered.
III. Insulated wire.

(a) I and II only (b) I and III only (c) I and II only (d) I, II and III

58.   An external antenna with a component comprised of a capacitor with a built-in shunt resistor that complies with the requirements for antenna isolating capacitors may be rated a minimum of ____ watts.

(a) 1/8 (b) 1/4 (c) .6 (d) 3

59. Glazed material of heat-treated or tempered glass may be protected by a single strip of foil extending completely across the top, at least ___ inches from the frame.

(a) 2 (b) 4 (c) 6 (d) 8

60. Showcases ___ feet or less in depth, as measured from the window to the main floor area of the premises may be protected utilizing the existing motion detection that is used to protect the main area of the premises.

(a) 1 1/2 (b) 2 (c) 3 (d) 3 1/2

61. Fine wire applied directly to a wood door that is in good condition and in a dry location shall be stapled at intervals not exceeding ___.

(a) 3" (b) 6" (c) 8" (d) 12"

62. All parts of an installation shall have a visual inspection and operational test at least each ___.

(a) year   (b) 2 years   (c) 3 years   (d) 5 years

63. A nonjacketed wire routed over a sharp corner or projection shall be protected from abrasion by ___ layers of electrical tape or the equivalent electrical insulation.

(a) 2   (b) 3   (c) 4   (d) 5

64. Openings on the same wall are accessible from a ledge that is between ____ to ____ wide, providing that the width of the ledge is at least one-fourth the vertical distance to the opening.

(a) one foot ... 4 feet   (b) one foot ... 3 1/2 feet   (c) 3 feet ... 3 feet   (d) none of these

65. A wire binding screw intended for connection to the line voltage source shall not be smaller than ____.

(a) #6   (b) #8   (c) #10   (d) none of these

66. The minimum size conductor for a telephone type wiring terminal is ____.

(a) #16   (b) #18   (c) #22   (d) #20

67. If leads are provided in lieu of wiring terminals, they shall not be less than ___ long.

(a) 4"   (b) 6"   (c) 8"   (d) 12"

68. Wires used outside buildings to connect the protected premises with a remote station shall be installed ___ for a holdup system.

(a) on poles   (b) with 8' clearance   (c) underground   (d) any of these

69. Alarm system wiring shall be spaced at least ___ from conductors of any electric light, power, of Class 3 circuits unless one of the circuits in conduit.

(a) 1"   (b) 2"   (c) 4"   (d) 12"

70. An alarm housing is considered to be "not more than ____ stories above street level."

(a) 4   (b) 5   (c) 3   (d) 2

71. A mechanical ringer shall give an indication automatically to the user when only ____ minutes operating power remains in the sounding device.

(a) 1   (b) 2   (c) 5   (d) 10

72. Interconnecting wiring shall not be smaller than # ____ AWG copper.

(a) 18   (b) 16   (c) 22   (d) 24

73. A grade A alarm system housing shall resist for a period of ____ minutes all attempts to silence the alarm by use of tools.

(a) 1   (b) 2   (c) 5   (d) 10

74. Contacts shall be installed so that a door cannot be opened more than ____ without initiating an alarm.

(a) 1"   (b) 2"   (c) 2 1/2"   (d) 3"

75. Foil shall be applied evenly and secured to the surface so that it will not blister or loosen in service. It shall be protected by a ___ covering or equivalent.

(a) conduit   (b) insulated   (c) varnish   (d) enamel

76. An acceptable source of electrical power for police station connected burglar alarm units is a rechargeable battery, this type of battery is also known as a ____ battery.

(a) wet-cell   (b) primary   (c) auxiliary   (d) secondary

77. A field wiring terminal shall be prevented from ____.

I. turning   II. being removed   III. shifting

(a) I and II   (b) II and III   (c) I and III   (d) I, II and III

78. A reverberant vault system shall be adjusted to transmit an alarm at sound levels of _____ decibels.

(a) 80 - 85   (b) 80 - 95   (c) 85 - 90   (d) 80 - 90

79. A grade A system with switches provided on the control unit by use of which the user can turn off portions of the protection or turn off the alarm, shall give a/an _____ indication to the user as long as the switches remain in the inoperative position.

I. audible II. prominent visual

(a) I only   (b) II only   (c) I or II   (d) none of these

80. The standby power supply shall maintain a central station and/or local mercantile automatically in the normal position for _____ hours.

(a) 4   (b) 12   (c) 24   (d) 36

OSHA

EXAM

100 QUESTIONS   **TIME LIMIT 5 HOURS**

KNOW YOUR FIRE EXTINGUISHERS

Public Safety Services
U.S.A. Non Governmental

(Seal: DEPARTMENT OF LABOR — UNITED STATES OF AMERICA)

	WATER TYPE				FOAM	CARBON DIOXIDE	DRY CHEMICAL			
	STORED PRESSURE	CARTRIDGE OPERATED	WATER PUMP TANK	SODA ACID	FOAM	CO² (PULL PIN-SQUEEZE LEVER)	SODIUM OR POTASSIUM BICARBONATE		MULTI-PURPOSE ABC	
							CARTRIDGE OPERATED	STORED PRESSURE	STORED PRESSURE	CARTRIDGE OPERATED
CLASS A FIRES — ORDINARY COMBUSTIBLES (WOOD, PAPER, TRASH HAVING GLOWING EMBERS)	YES	YES	YES	YES	YES	NO (BUT WILL CONTAIN SMALL SURFACE FIRES)	NO (BUT WILL CONTROL SMALL SURFACE FIRES)	NO (BUT WILL CONTROL SMALL SURFACE FIRES)	YES	YES
CLASS B FIRES — FLAMMABLE LIQUIDS (GASOLINE, OIL, PAINTS, GREASE, ETC.)	NO	NO	NO	NO	YES	YES	YES	YES	YES	YES
CLASS C FIRES — ELECTRICAL EQUIPMENT	NO	NO	NO	NO	NO	YES	YES	YES	YES	YES
CLASS D FIRES — COMBUSTIBLE METALS	SPECIAL EXTINGUISHING AGENTS APPROVED BY RECOGNIZED TESTING LABORATORIES									
METHOD OF OPERATION	PULL PIN- SQUEEZE HANDLE	TURN UPSIDE DOWN AND BUMP	PUMP HANDLE	TURN UPSIDE DOWN	TURN UPSIDE DOWN	PULL PIN- SQUEEZE LEVER	RUPTURE CARTRIDGE SQUEEZE LEVER	PIN PULL SQUEEZE HANDLE	PULL PIN- SQUEEZE HANDLE	RUPTURE CARTRIDGE SQUEEZE LEVER
RANGE	30'-40'	30'-40'	30'-40'	30'-40'	30'-40'	3'-8'	5'-20'	5'-20'	5'-20'	5'-20'
MAINTENANCE	CHECK AIR PRESSURE GAUGE MONTHLY	WEIGH GAS CARTRIDGE ADD WATER IF REQUIRED ANNUALLY	DISCHARGE AND FILL WITH WATER ANNUALLY	DISCHARGE ANNUALLY RECHARGE	DISCHARGE ANNUALLY RECHARGE	WEIGHT SEMI ANNUALLY	WEIGH GAS CARTRIDGE CHECK CONDITION OF DRY CHEMICAL ANNUALLY	CHECK PRESSURE GAUGE AND CONDITION OF DRY CHEMICAL ANNUALLY	CHECK PRESSURE GAUGE AND CONDITION OF DRY CHEMICAL ANNUALLY	WEIGH GAS CARTRIDGE CHECK CONDITION OF DRY CHEMICAL ANNUALLY

Fire class symbols: **B** FLAMMABLE LIQUIDS — **C** ELECTRICAL EQUIPMENT

100 QUESTIONS   **TIME LIMIT 5 HOURS**

1. Receptacles on a two-wire, single-phase portable or vehicle-mounted generator rated not more than ____ kw, where the circuit conductors of the generator are insulated from the generator frame and all other grounded surfaces, need not be protected with GFCI.

(a) 2 (b) 5 (c) 10 (d) 15

2. On power transmission and distribution the minimum clear hot stick distance is that for the use of live-line tools held by linemen when performing live-line work. For a 169 kv line phase to phase the distance would be ____.

(a) 3' 4" (b) 3' 6" (c) 3' 8" (d) 5'

3. Oil-filled transformers shall not be used in underground mines unless they are located in a fire-resistant enclosure and surrounded by a ____ to contain the contents of the transformer in the event of a rupture.

(a) fence (b) dike (c) barrier (d) wall

4. Unless installed in a complete metallic raceway, each branch circuit shall contain a separate equipment grounding conductor, and all receptacles shall be electrically connected to the grounding conductor.

(a) true (b) false

5. Employees shall be provided with eye and face protection equipment when machines or operations present potential eye or face injury from ____ agents.

I. radiation II. chemical III. physical

(a) I only (b) II only (c) II and III (d) I, II and III

6. A____ means a rope, suitable for supporting one person.

(a) safety belt (b) lanyard (c) contaminant (d) none of these

7. Caution signs shall be used only to ____.

I. caution against unsafe practice   II. warn against potential hazards

(a) I only   (b) II only   (c) either I or II   (d) neither I nor II

8. According to OSHA regulations, the maximum span of 2" x 10" undressed lumber on a scaffold when loaded with 50 p.s.f. is ____ feet.

(a) 4   (b) 6   (c) 8   (d) 10

9. According to OSHA regulations, exposure to impulsive or impact noise should not exceed ____ dB peak sound pressure level.

(a) 70   (b) 115   (c) 130   (d) 140

10. One toilet shall be provided at the construction job site for a maximum of ____ employees.

(a) 10   (b) 15   (c) 20   (d) 24

11. According to OSHA regulations, lifelines used for employee safeguarding shall have a minimum breaking strength of ____ pounds.

(a) 5000   (b) 5400   (c) 6200   (d) 7800

12. Bell bottom pier hole, means a type of shaft or footing excavation where the top is made larger than the cross section.

(a) true   (b) false

13. The minimum illumination of an indoor warehouse is ____ foot-candles.

(a) 2   (b) 3   (c) 4   (d) 5

14. Toprails shall be capable of withstanding, without failure a force of at least ___ lbs for guardrail systems installed on single-point adjustable suspension scaffolds.

(a) 25   (b) 50   (c) 100   (d) 200

15. In work areas where the exact location of underground electric power lines is unknown, employees using jack-hammers, bars, or other hand tools which may contact a line shall be provided with ____.

(a) rubber mats   (b) double-insulated tools   (c) insulated protective gloves   (d) none of these

16. When work is to be performed in a manhole or unvented vault, no entry shall be permitted unless forced ventilation is provided or the atmosphere is found to be safe by testing for oxygen deficiency and the presence of ____.

I. fumes   II. explosive gases

(a) I only   (b) II only   (c) either I or II   (d) neither I nor II

17. Any openings cut in a floor for the disposal of materials shall be no larger in size than ____ percent of the aggregate of the total floor area, unless the lateral supports of the removed flooring remain in place.

(a) 10   (b) 15   (c) 20   (d) 25

18. The minimum intensity of light on any walkway, ladder, stairway, or working level in compressed-air chambers shall not be less than ____ foot-candles.

(a) 10   (b) 12   (c) 15   (d) 20

19. During the final placing of solid web structural members, the load shall not be released from the hoisting line until the members are secured with not less than ___ bolts, or the equivalent at each connection and drawn up wrench tight.

(a) two   (b) three   (c) four   (d) none of these

20. Inside of buildings, cylinders shall be stored in a well protected, well ventilated, dry location, at least ___ feet from highly combustible materials such as oil or excelsior.

(a) 5   (b) 10   (c) 15   (d) 20

21. Clearance of at least _____ inches shall be maintained between the top level of the stored material and the sprinkler deflectors.

(a) 36   (b) 24   (c) 18   (d) 12

22. Toeboards shall be equivalent in strength to 1" by ___ lumber.

(a) 4"   (b) 5"   (c) 6"   (d) 8"

23. The rungs of ladder-type platforms shall be made of _____.

I. hickory   II. oak   III. ash

(a) I only   (b) II only   (c) III only   (d) I, II and III

24. A potassium bicarbonate fire extinguisher can be used to extinguish an electrical fire.

(a) true   (b) false

25. The term _____ means separated from other conducting surfaces by a dielectric substance (including air space) offering a high resistance to the passage of current.

(a) dielectric strength   (b) insulated   (c) covered   (d) coated

26. Construction areas, ramps, runways, corridors, offices, shops and storage areas shall be lighted to not less than the minimum illumination intensities listed in _____ while work is in progress.

(a) Table L-3   (b) Table D-3   (c) Appendix B   (d) Section IV

27. Any employee on the job site may operate a powder actuated tool.

(a) true   (b) false

28. Signaling by flaggers and the use of flaggers including warning garments worn by flaggers shall conform to Part V of the manual on Uniform Traffic Control Devices.

(a) true   (b) false

29. Extension cords shall not be _____.

I. suspended by wire   II. hung from nails   III. fastened with staples

(a) I only   (b) II only   (c) III only   (d) I, II and III

30. All fabric and leather used for lineman's safety straps shall be tested for leakage current and shall not exceed 1 milliampere when a potential of _____ volts is applied to the electrodes positioned 12" apart.

(a) 1000   (b) 3000   (c) 5000   (d) 10,000

31. When employees are required to work within a structure to be demolished which has been damaged by fire, flood, explosion, or other cause, the walls or floor shall be _____.

I. braced   II. shored

(a) I only   (b) II only   (c) either I or II   (d) neither I nor II

32. Every motor vehicle or conveyance used for transporting explosives shall be marked or placarded on both sides, the front, and the rear with the word "EXPLOSIVES" in red letters, not less than _____ inches in height, on white background.

(a) 2   (b) 4   (c) 6   (d) 8

33. At least two designated people shall be on duty above ground whenever any employee is working underground.

(a) true   (b) false

34. Cranes mounted on rail tracks shall be equipped with _____ limiting the travel of the crane on the track and stops or buffers at each end of the tracks.

(a) stop switches   (b) relays   (c) limit switches   (d) pressure switches

35. Plank type platforms shall be composed of not less than nominal 2 x 8 inch unspliced planks, connected together on the underside with cleats at intervals not exceeding _____ feet starting 6 inches from the end.

(a) 4   (b) 6   (c) 8   (d) 10

36. When compressed gas cylinders are hoisted, they shall be secured by ___.

I. cradle   II. slingboard   III. choaker slings

(a) I only   (b) II only   (c) I and II only   (d) I, II, or III

37. Which of the following shall **not** be used as a ground return for arc welding?

I.   conduits containing electrical circuits
II.   metal structural frame of building
III. pipelines containing gases or flammable liquids

(a) I only   (b) I and II   (c) I and III   (d) III only

38. Powered circular saws without positive accessory holding means, shall be equipped with a ____ switch that will shut off the power when the pressure is released.

(a) single-pole   (b) two-way   (c) double-pole   (d) constant pressure

39. The employer shall keep ____ record of all measurements taken to monitor employee exposure to asbestos.

(a) a daily   (b) a semi-annual   (c) an accurate   (d) a monthly

40. Should a safety belt be subjected to inservice loading, the safety belt should be immediately removed from service and shall not be used again for employee safeguarding.

(a) true   (b) false

41. The responsibility to initiate and maintain accident prevention programs lies with the ____.

(a) contractor   (b) employer   (c) safety department   (d) maintenance department

42. When employees are required to be in trenches four feet deep or more, an adequate means of exit, such as a ladder or steps, shall be provided and located so as to require no more than ____ feet of lateral travel.

(a) 25   (b) 20   (c) 15   (d) 10

43. Single-throw knife switches shall be so connected that the blades are dead when the switch is in the closed position.

(a) true   (b) false

44. A fire extinguisher, rated not less than 10B shall be provided within ____ feet of wherever more than 5 gallons of flammable or combustible liquids or 5 pounds of flammable gas are being used on the job site.

(a) 25   (b) 50   (c) 1000   (d) 500

45. Illumination in general construction area is a minimum of ____ foot-candles.

(a) 3   (b) 5   (c) 10   (d) none of these

46. A bricklayer's square scaffold shall not exceed five feet in height, ____ feet in width.

(a) 3   (b) 4   (c) 5   (d) 6

47. All new safety nets shall meet accepted performance such as 17,500 foot pounds minimum impact resistance.

(a) true   (b) false

48. Facilities for quick drenching of the eyes and body shall be provided within ____ feet of the battery handling areas.

(a) 10   (b) 12   (c) 20   (d) 25

49. On power transmission and distribution the distance would be ____ phase to phase for live-line bare hand work on a 169 kv phase to phase distribution.

(a) 3' 6"   (b) 3' 8"   (c) 5' 6"   (d) 8' 4"

50. Single-rail ladders shall not exceed ____ feet in length.

(a) 0   (b) 50   (c) 36   (d) 32

51. OSHA regulations state that shore or lean-to scaffolding is prohibited.

(a) true   (b) false

52. The lift controls on extendible and articulating boom platform and bucket trucks shall be tested ____ to determine that such controls are in safe working condition.

(a) daily   (b) biweekly   (c) weekly   (d) monthly

53. Each employee on a walking/working surface (horizontal and vertical surface) with an unprotected side or edge which is ___ feet or more above a lower level shall be protected from falling by the use of guard rails, safety nets, or personal fall arrest systems.

(a) 3   (b) 6   (c) 10   (d) 12

54. Material shall not be stored within ____ of a fire door.

(a) 3'   (b) 30"   (c) 48"   (d) 32"

55. Material stored inside buildings under construction shall not be placed within ___ feet of any hoistway or inside floor openings.

(a) 6   (b) 8   (c) 10   (d) 12

56. The minimum clear distance between the sides of individual-rung/step ladders and the minimum clear distance between the side rails of other fixed ladders shall be ____ inches.

(a) 16   (b) 18   (c) 20   (d) 24

57. The maximum permissible noise exposure is ____ hours per day at 97 dBA slow response.

(a) 3   (b) 4   (c) 5   (d) 6

58. Employees working in areas where there is a possible danger of head injury from _____ shall be protected by protective helmets.

I. electrical shock or burn   II. impact   III. falling or flying objects

(a) II and III   (b) I and III   (c) I and II   (d) I, II and III

59. When firing a circuit of electric blasting caps, care must be exercised to ensure that _____ of delivered current is available, in accordance with the manufacturer's recommendations.

(a) 2 amperes   (b) the full amount   (c) an adequate quantity   (d) half

60. All wells or shafts over _____ feet in depth shall be supported by steel casing.

(a) 10   (b) 25   (c) 15   (d) 5

61. The supply of fresh air shall not be less than _____ cubic feet per minute for each employee underground.

(a) 50   (b) 100   (c) 150   (d) 200

62. Where doors or gates open directly on a stairway, a platform shall be provided, and the swing of the door shall not reduce the effective width of the platform to less than _____ inches.

(a) 36   (b) 30   (c) 24   (d) 20

63. No welding, cutting, or heating shall be done where the application of _____ creates a hazard.

I. heavy dust concentrations   II. flammable compounds   III. flammable paints

(a) I only   (b) II only   (c) III only   (d) I, II and III

64. Soda-acid type extinguishers may be used on Class C fires.

(a) true   (b) false

65. The minimum clear distance between side rails for all portable ladders shall be _____ inches.

(a) 5 1/2   (b) 8 1/2   (c) 11 1/2   (d) 14 1/2

66. Wire rope shall not be used for material handling if in any length of _____ diameters the total number of visible broken wires exceeds 10% of the total number of wires.

(a) 6   (b) 8   (c) 10   (d) 12

67. OSHA requires for skeleton steel construction that no more than 48 feet or _____ floors of unfinished bolting or welding exist.

(a) two   (b) three   (c) four   (d) five

68. The maximum allowable slope for type B soil is _____ degrees.

(a) 33   (b) 45   (c) 90   (d) none of these

69. Where electrical transmission lines are energized and rated at 50 kv or less, a clearance of _____ minimum must be maintained by the crane and load.

(a) 6' 6''   (b) 8'   (c) 10'   (d) 15'

70. All firefighting equipment, provided by the employer, shall be _____.

(a) readily accessible   (b) conspicuously located
(c) not over 4' from floor level   (d) none of these

71. Rigging equipment for material handling shall be inspected _____ and as necessary during its use to ensure that it is safe.

(a) each 30 days   (b) at the end of the work day
(c) prior to use on each shift   (d) at least every 10 working days

72. Safety nets shall be provided when work places are more than _____ feet above ground or water, where the use of ladders, scaffolds, safety lines, or belts, etc., is impractical.

(a) 12   (b) 20   (c) 25   (d) 30

73. Lifelines shall be secured above the point of operation to an anchorage or structural member capable of supporting a minimum dead weight of _____ pounds.

(a) 1500   (b) 3600   (c) 5400   (d) 6000

74. All hose in use, carrying acetylene, oxygen, natural or manufactured fuel gas, or any gas substance which may ignite or enter into combustion, or be in any way harmful to employees, shall be _____.

I. inspected at the beginning of each working shift
II. inspected at the end of each working shift

(a) I only   (b) II only   (c) both I and II   (d) neither I nor II

75. On power transmission and distribution rubber protective equipment shall be visually inspected prior to use. In addition, _____ test shall be performed for rubber gloves prior to use.

(a) a dielectric   (b) an electrical   (c) a water   (d) an air

76. A _____ is an airtight structure separating the working chamber from free air or from another chamber under a lesser pressure than the working pressure.

(a) caisson   (b) bulkhead   (c) decanting   (d) safety screen

77. A body belt shall be worn and a/an _____ attached to the boom or basket when working from an aerial lift.

(a) putlog   (b) outrigger   (c) contaminant   (d) lanyard

78. Scaffold end platforms 10 feet or less in length shall not extend over its support more than ___ inches unless other conditions for safety apply.

(a) 8   (b) 10   (c) 12   (d) 24

79. A medium duty tube and coupler scaffold shall have all posts, bearers, runners and bracing of nominal _____ inch OD steel tubing.

(a) 1   (b) 1 1/2   (c) 2   (d) 2 1/2

80. A clearance of _____ shall be maintained around the path of travel of fire doors unless a barricade is provided, in which case no clearance is required.

(a) 2' (b) 30'' (c) 20'' (d) 3'

81. If the personnel hoist wire rope speed is 300 feet per minute the minimum rope safety factor must be _____.

(a) 8.75 (b) 9.2 (c) 9.5 (d) 10

82. The term "rops" means rope operating protective standards.

(a) true (b) false

83. A Class C fire is a(an) _____ type fire.

(a) caustic (b) combustible (c) flammable liquid (d) electrical

84. No more than _____ gallons of flammable or combustible liquids shall be stored in a room outside of an approved storage cabinet.

(a) 10 (b) 25 (c) 30 (d) 50

85. Before heat is applied to a drum, container, or hollow structure, a _____ shall be provided for the release of any built-up pressure during the application of heat.

(a) pressure relief valve (b) exhaust fan (c) vent or opening (d) none of these

86. Unstable objects such as _____ shall not be used to support scaffolds or planks.

I. barrels II. boxes III. loose brick or concrete blocks

(a) I only (b) II only (c) III only (d) I, II and III

87. The vertical height of a guard rail shall be approximately _____ inches.

(a) 24 (b) 30 (c) 36 (d) 42

88. The proper maintenance for a multi-purpose ABC dry chemical stored pressure fire extinguisher is to ____.

(a) weigh it each 12 months
(b) check pressure gauge and condition of dry chemical semi-annually
(c) check pressure gauge monthly
(d) check pressure gauge and condition of dry chemical annually

89. Bricklayer's square scaffolds shall not exceed ____ tiers in height and shall be so constructed and arranged that one square shall rest directly above the other.

(a) 3 (b) 4 (c) 5 (d) 6

90. Detonators shall be short-circuited in holes which have been ____ until wired into the blasting circuit.

I. shunted II. primed

(a) I only (b) II only (c) both I and II (d) neither I nor II

91. On multi-story structures, perimeter ___ shall be installed at the final interior and exterior perimeters of the floors as soon as the metal decking has been installed.

(a) safety valves (b) weatherproofing (c) elevators (d) safety cables

92. No sidewalk shall be undermined unless a support system or another method is provided to protect employees.

(a) true (b) false

93. A hole is a gap or void ___ inches or more in its least dimension, in a floor, rood or other walking/ working surface.

(a) 12 (b) 6 (c) 3 (d) 2

94. All ladder jack scaffolds shall be limited to light duty and shall not exceed a height of ____ feet above the floor or ground.

(a) 15   (b) 20   (c) 24   (d) 30

95. Extension cord sets used with portable electric tools and appliances shall be of two-wire type and shall be designed for hard or extra-hard usage.

(a) true   (b) false

96. When working over water or near water, ring buoys with at least 90 feet of line shall be provided and readily available for emergency rescue operations. Distance between ring buoys shall not exceed ____ feet.

(a) 50   (b) 100   (c) 150   (d) 200

97. The minimum illumination intensity in foot-candles for general construction plants and shops is ____.

(a) 3   (b) 5   (c) 10   (d) 12

98. A fire extinguisher, rated not less than 2A, shall be provided for each ____ square feet of the protected building area, or major fraction thereof.

(a) 1500   (b) 3000   (c) 5000   (d) 10,000

99. Not more than ____ persons shall be permitted at one time upon a pump jack scaffold between any two supports.

(a) 1   (b) 2   (c) 3   (d) 4

100. The first aid kit shall consist of materials in a weatherproof container with individually sealed packages for each type of item.

(a) true   (b) false

BUSINESS

LAW

FLORIDA UNEMPLOYMENT COMPENSATION

1. An employee is responsible for paying _____ % of the Florida Unemployment Compensation Tax?

(a) 5   (b) 0   (c) 10   (d) none of these

2. When an employer buys an additional unit of business from another liable employer, the purchaser must submit Form _____ marked "AMENDED" to provide additional information concerning the purchase.

(a) DR-1   (b) DR-3   (c) DR-7   (d) DDR-1

3. Generally, a business is liable for Federal Unemployment Tax in the current or preceding calendar year if the employer has paid at least _____ in wages in one calendar quarter or has had at least _____ employee at any time in each of 20 different calendar weeks in a year.

(a) 1500 ... 2   (b) 1500 ... 1   (c) 1250 ... 2   (d) 1250 ... 1

4. A new employer has paid $9,000 to an employee during a calendar year. According to the Florida Unemployment Compensation what would the Florida Unemployment Tax be?

(a) $243   (b) $270   (c) $135   (d) $189

5. An employer has not reported and paid on time, therefore the credit is limited to _____ percent of the amount which would have been allowable as a credit had the state tax been paid on time.

(a) 50   (b) 30   (c) 60   (d) 90

6. An employer can receive the maximum credit of _____ percent against the Federal Unemployment Tax, for timely payments and reports to the State.

(a) 2.7   (b) 3.5   (c) 5.4   (d) 6.2

7. Completed tax reports must be mailed to the Bureau of Tax even though the tax due is less than _____.

(a) $1   (b) $10   (c) $5   (d) $25

8. An employer failed to file his report to the Bureau of Unemployment Compensation. What was the penalty charge after 90 days?

(a) $30   (b) $75   (c) $5   (d) $10

9. An employer will not be charged unemployment benefits for an employee under which of the following circumstances?

(a) failed without good cause to apply for suitable work
(b) suspended or discharged for misconduct at work
(c) voluntarily quit without good cause
(d) all of the above

10. The weekly benefit amount is ___ of the high quarter wages.

(a) 1/12th   (b) 1/26th   (c) 1/46th   (d) 1/75th

11. An exempt employer who voluntarily elects coverage under the Unemployment Compensation Law must remain covered for a minimum period of at least ____ .

(a) four years   (b) two years   (c) one year   (d) five years

12. The first ____ in wages paid to every employee during a calendar year is taxable.

(a) $9000   (b) $5000   (c) $6000   (d) $7000

13.An employer has become liable for the payment of taxes, his beginning tax rate is ____ and will not change until the employer has reported for ____ quarters.

(a) .270 .... four   (b) .0270 .... ten   (c) .0270 ... five   (d) .270 ... five

14. Employer tax rate notices are normally mailed to employers immediately prior to the tax rate effective date. If the employer wishes to protest the assigned tax rate, it must be in writing within 30 days from the date of receiving the UCT-20.

(a) true   (b) false

15. Benefit payments made to any eligible claimant shall be charged to the taxpaying employer's experience rating record when the employer paid the individual wages of ___ or more within the base period of the claim.

(a) $20   (b) $25   (c) $50   (d) $100

16. All unemployment compensation claimants are audited every other quarter by using the most current employer wage records.

(a) true   (b) false

17. If an new owner purchases a business, the division must be notified using form ___.

(a) UCS-7   (b) UCS-1   (c) UCS-3   (d) UCT-6

18. An employers account is eligible for termination if the liability requirements have been met for the entire calendar year.

(a) true   (b) false

19. Sometime during the last week of every calendar quarter pre-printed tax and wage report form, ____ is mailed to every liable employer to fill out and return to the Bureau of Tax.

(a) UCT-6   (b) UCS-6   (c) UCT-7   (d) UCS-3

20. When an employer conducts business in one or more locations, completion of form ____, Multiple Worksite Report, is required on a quarterly basis.

(a) UCT-14   (b) BRI-3S   (c) UCT-14R   (d) BLS-3020

1. The term "child" refers to a child legally adopted after the injury of the employee.

(a) true   (b) false

2. In the event of any injury resulting in death, the employer shall notify the Division within ____ hours by telephone or telegraph.

(a) 8   (b) 12   (c) 24   (d) 36

3. Under workers' compensation law, when an injury is caused by the willful refusal of the employee to use a safety device or to observe a safety rule or statute, the _____.

(a) compensation can be reduced by 50%
(b) compensation can be reduced by 25%
(c) no compensation shall be paid
(d) compensation can be reduced by 75%

4. The term "casual" refers only to employments when the work contemplated is to be completed in not exceeding ____ working days and when the total labor cost of such work is less than $ ____.

(a) 20 ... 200   (b) 10 ... 500   (c) 10 ... 200   (d) 20 ... 100

5. No compensation is normally allowed for the first 7 days of disability.

(a) true   (b) false

6. If death results from the accident within one year thereafter or follows continuous disability and results from the accident within five years thereafter, the employer shall pay ____.

(a) actual funeral expenses not to exceed $7,500
(b) to a childless spouse, 50% of the average weekly wage until spouse's death
(c) 33 1/3% of the average weekly wage to all dependents at the time of death
(d) any of the above may apply

7. Compensation for disability resulting from injuries shall not be less than ____ per week.

(a) $20 (b) $30 (c) $10 (d) $40

8. The employee shall give the employer notice of an injury within ____ days after the date of such injury.

(a) 7 (b) 30 (c) 10 (d) 15

9. If a 16 year old student is working part-time and is injured on the construction site, the workers' compensation benefits ___.

(a) shall not be paid
(b) may be twice the amount normally due, and the employer alone is responsible for the additional amount
(c) the additional amount of compensation due will be paid equally by the employer and the carrier
(d) none of these

10. Benefits for temporary partial disability shall be paid during the continuance of such disability, not to exceed a period of ____ years.

(a) 2 (b) 5 (c) 7 (d) 10

11. Within ____ days of actual knowledge of injury or death, the employer shall report same to carrier.

(a) 5 (b) 7 (c) 10 (d) 14

12. The term "accident" means which of the following?

(a) a mental or nervous injury
(b) death due to the habitual use of alcohol or narcotic drugs
(c) an unexpected or unusual event or result, happening suddenly
(d) all of the above

13. A report to the Workers' Compensation Division for injury or death, filed by the employer, must provide which of the following?

(a) name, address, and business of the employer
(b) the year, month, day and hour when the injury or death occurred
(c) the name, social security number and occupation of the employee
(d) all of the above

14. The first payment of compensation for total disability or death will become due on the _____ day after the employer has knowledge of the injury or death.

(a) 7th   (b) 14th   (c) 21st   (d) 28th

15. If any compensation, payable under the terms of an award, is not paid within _____ days after it becomes due, _____ shall be added to any unpaid compensation.

(a) 7 ... 20%   (b) 15 ... 20%   (c) 20 ... 15%   (d) 20 ... 30%

16. If the employer has made advance payments of compensation, he shall be entitled to be reimbursed out of any unpaid installment or installments of compensation due.

(a) true   (b) false

17. The time for notice of injury or death provided in s.440.185(1) shall be extended in cases of occupational diseases to a period of 120 days.

(a) true   (b) false

18. Employee includes any person who is an officer of a corporation and who performs services for remuneration for such corporation within the state of Florida, whether or not such services are continuous.

(a) true   (b) false

19. The term "parent" does not include which of the following?

(a) parents-in-law
(b) stepparents
(c) any person who for less than 3 years prior to the death of the deceased employee stood
in the place of a parent to him and were dependent on the injured employee
(d) all of the above

20. "Adoption" or "Adopted" means legal adoption prior to or immediately following the time of the injury.

(a) true   (b) false

CIRCULAR E

1. Which of the following kinds of payments are not subject to social security?

I.   payments made more than 3 months after the last calendar month in which the employee worked
II. payments received under the railroad retirement act
III. payments received under a workmen's compensation law

(a) I and II   (b) II and III   (c) I and III   (d) I, II and III

2. Underpayments of the amount required to be deposited may subject you to the failure to deposit penalty. The penalty is _____ of the underpayment if more than 15 days late.

(a) 25%   (b) 7%   (c) 12%   (d) 10%

3. Each new employee must complete and sign which form?

(a) W-5   (b) W-4   (c) W-2   (d) W-3

4. When figuring social security taxes for the year, withhold _____ from each wage payment until you reach the wage base limit.

(a) 10%   (b) 6.2%   (c) 20%   (d) 5.71%

5. The old-age, survivors, disability, and disability insurance part is financed by ___.

I. the medicare tax   II. the social security tax   III. the income tax

(a) I only   (b) II only   (c) III only   (d) I and II

6. If an employer had _____ or more employees at any time in each of any 20 calendar weeks, he is required to file a return of Form 940 Federal Unemployment Tax Act.

(a) 1   (b) 2   (c) 3   (d) 4

7. The employer identification number is a nine digit number issued by the IRS.

(a) true   (b) false

8. An electrician is married, claims one deduction and is paid $475 per week. What is his take home pay?

(a) $413.66   (b) $370.50   (c) $390.88   (d) $323

9. An employer can request an employer identification number on Form SS-4.

(a) true   (b) false

10. A penalty of _____ may be assessed when an employer overstates the amount of his Federal taxes to be deposited.

(a) 0%   (b) 25%   (c) 50%   (d) 100%

11. For Federal Unemployment Tax purposes, "employer" refers to any person or organization that during this year or last year paid wages of _____ or more in any calendar quarter.

(a) $2500   (b) $1250   (c) $750   (d) $1500

12. An employee is single, claims no dependents and is paid $325 per week. What is his take home pay?

(a) $246.50   (b) $266.14   (c) $260.44   (d) $214

13. All employment tax records should be kept for at least _____ years.

(a) 4   (b) 7   (c) 5   (d) 10

14. When an employer fails to make the required Federal income tax deposits on time within 5 days late a penalty of _____ may be assessed to the underdeposited taxes.

(a) 25%   (b) 15%   (c) 2%   (d) 5%

15. For deposit purposes, figure Federal unemployment taxes _____.

(a) monthly   (b) quarterly   (c) bi-annually   (d) annually

16. If your total FUTA tax liability is $500 or less at the end of any quarter _____.

I.   no deposit is required
II. deposit is due within 15 days after the end of the month
III. you may carry the taxes over to the following quarter

(a) I and II   (b) II and III   (c) I and III   (d) I, II and III

17. When you don't have a payroll period, withhold the tax as if you paid wages on a daily or miscellaneous payroll period. Figure the number of days, including Sundays and Holidays, in the period covered by the wage payment.

(a) true   (b) false

18. Federal Tax Deposit Coupon, Form _____ is used to deposit employment taxes and all other types of taxes that are deposited.

(a) 941   (b) 8109   (c) 940   (d) 2106

19. An employer must make advance EIC payments to employees who correctly fill out Form _____.

(a) W-2   (b) W-3   (c) W-4   (d) W-5

20. If an employee quits working for you before the end of the year, you may give him Form W-2 any time after employment ends but not later than January 31 of the following year.

(a) true   (b) false

FAIR LABOR STANDARDS ACT

1. The payment of federal employee rates and fringe benefits on federally financed construction contracts is required by the ____.

(a) **Davis-Bacon Act**
(b) **Walsh-Healey Act**
(c) **contract work hours and Safety Standards Act**
(d) **Wage Garnishment Law**

2. It is a violation of the Fair Labor Standards Act (FLSA) to fire or discriminate against an employee who files a complaint. Willful violations can be prosecuted criminally and subject to a fine up to ____.

(a) **$1000** (b) **$5000** (c) **$10,000** (d) **$15,000**

3. According to the Fair Labor Standards Act employers must maintain records EXCEPT for ____.

(a) **total wages paid**
(b) **total number of hours worked each day**
(c) **employees birthdate if over 19 years of age**
(d) **any deductions to employees pay**

4. If a roofer is paid $20 per square, and it took 50 hours to install 20 squares, his gross pay would be ____.

(a) **$400.00** (b) **$400.40** (c) **$440.00** (d) **$520.00**

5. The minimum wage effective July 24, 2009 is ____ per hour.

(a) **$4.75** (b) **$5.25** (c) **$6.15** (d) **$7.25**

6. An employee is paid $8.00 per hour and works 44 hours in a workweek. The employee is entitled to at least one and one half times $8.00 or $13.00 for each hour over 40.

(a) **true** (b) **false**

7. A supervisor is salaried at $600 per week for a specified 40 hours per week. The job requires the supervisor to work 8 hours on Saturday a normal day off. What would be his gross pay?

(a) **$600** (b) **$720** (c) **$780** (d) **$820**

8. If a dry wall installer is paid $1.50 per board and installs 400 boards in 50 hours, his gross pay would be ____.

(a) $825   (b) $660   (c) $600   (d) $720

9. Violations of the youth employment provisions are subject to a civil penalty of up to ____ for each employee who was subject of a violation.

(a) $1,000   (b) $2,000   (c) $5,000   (d) $11,000

10. Under the Child Labor Laws , youths 14 and 15 years old may work ____ hours per day, outside school hours in various nonmanufacturing, nonmining, nonhazardous jobs.

(a) no more than 3 hours on a school day
(b) 20 hours in a school week
(c) unlimited hours on a nonschool day
(d) unlimited hours on a nonschool week

Chapter 489, Part II - Rules 61 G6 - Chapter 633

1. The initial application and examination fee for certification of electrical contractors is no more than _____.

(a) $75 (b) $200 (c) $400 (d) $450

2. For reactivating a license, the continuing education requirements shall not exceed _____ classroom hours for each year the license was inactive.

(a) 12 (b) 14 (c) 16 (d) 18

3. Any license which is inactive for more than 10 years shall be automatically suspended.

(a) true (b) false

4. The Electrical Contractor's Licensing Board consists of eleven members. _____ are to be certified electrical contractors, _____ are consumer members, one certified alarm system contractor, and one a certified specialty electrical contractor.

(a) 7 ... 2 (b) 6 ... 3 (c) 2 ... 7 (d) 3 ... 6

5. Which of the following penalties may be imposed upon any electrical contractor by the board?

(a) issuance of a reprimand
(b) impose an administrative fine not to exceed $10,000 for each count or separate offense
(c) revoke or suspend a certificate or registration
(d) all of the above

6. When an applicant wishes to do business as a sole proprietorship, the certificate, when granted, will be in the name of that applicant only.

(a) true (b) false

7. A disciplined alarm system contractor may be reissued a certificate or registration by the department upon certification by the board that he has complied with all of the terms and conditions set forth in the final order.

(a) true   (b) false

8. After the initial appointment of the board by the Governor, the members shall be appointed for _____ year terms.

(a) one   (b) two   (c) three   (d) four

9. Which of the following are exempt from the construction licensing law?

(a) an officer appointed by a court when he is acting within the scope of his/her office as defined by law or court order
(b) the installation of alarm systems on motor vehicles and boats
(c) a registered architect acting in his professional capacity
(d) all of the above

10. The person taking over an incomplete contract shall notify the appropriate board of his name and address within ___ days after the death of the contractor.

(a) 10   (b) 14   (c) 20   (d) 30

11. The failure of a contractor to perform work without just cause for _____ consecutive days shall create a presumption that the contractor has abandoned the job.

(a) 30   (b) 45   (c) 60   (d) 90

12. Upon the termination of your only certified qualifier, you shall notify the board and you will have a period of _____ days from the individuals termination to qualify another person.

(a) 21   (b) 30   (c) 60   (d) 90

13. The Electrical Contractors' Licensing Board and the Construction Industry Licensing Board shall each appoint a committee to meet jointly at least four times a year.

(a) true   (b) false

14. Disciplinary proceedings may be instituted for ____.

(a) practicing on a inactive certificate or registration
(b) upon proof that the licensee is guilty of misconduct
(c) willfully or deliberately violating the applicable building codes
(d) all of the above

15. A Board member, attending official meetings of the Board, receives $ ____ per day for compensation.

(a) 25   (b) 50   (c) 75   (d) 100

16. A credit report on the business organization from any recognized credit bureau is required to be dated within twelve months of the date of filing of the application.

(a) true   (b) false

17. The minimum amount of liability insurance required as a prerequisite to the issuance of a certificate is $ ____ per person $500,000 Property Damage or $ ____ for minimum combined single limit policy.

(a) 100,000 ... 800,000   **(b) 300,000 ... 100,000**
(c) 200,000 ... 400,000   **(d) 400,000 ... 200,000**

18. An applicant who fails the certification exam may take the next subsequent exam upon payment of the re-examination fee.

(a) true   (b) false

19. The initial application fee for the certification examination for alarm systems contractor is $200.

(a) true   (b) false

20. The re-examination fee for Technical/Safety certification is $200.

(a) true   (b) false

21. The initial fee for registration is $200.

(a) true   (b) false

22. To service, recharge, repair, install, or inspect all types of fire extinguishers, including recharging carbon dioxide units and conducting hydrostatic tests on water, water chemical, and dry chemical types of extinguishers only; a ____ license is required.

(a) Class B   (b) Class 2   (c) Class 4   (d) Class C

23. The State Fire Marshal shall have the right to inspect any fire control system during and after construction to determine that such system meets the standards set forth in the laws and rules of the state.

(a) true   (b) false

24. Every fire safety inspector certificate is valid for a period of ____ years from the date of issuance.

(a) two   (b) three   (c) four   (d) five

25. The firefighter training program shall consist of not less than ____ hours.

(a) 100   (b) 160   (c) 220   (d) 360

26. An order of suspension or revocation of a license or permit from the State Fire Marshal may not exceed ____ for the suspension and ____ for the revocation.

(a) one year .... lifetime   (b) two years ... lifetime
(c) two years ... five years   (d) two years ... two years

1. ___ summarize your operation's activity for a certain period, usually a month, a quarter, a year or more, and show its status at the end of that period.

(a) Net worth   (b) Current assets   (c) Financial statements   (d) Net Quick

2. You received a $8,000.00 payment which represents one-half of the total contract price. You know that the job is only 40% complete. What is your balance, unearned income?

(a) $6,400   (b) $1,600   (c) $9,600   (d) $8,000

3. For builders, keeping records is required by law.

(a) true   (b) false

4. Form ___ summarizes taxable wages and provides for payment of any income taxes or FICA due.

(a) 501   (b) 941   (c) 508   (d) none of these

5. Payroll taxes can be variable or fixed expenses.

(a) true   (b) false

6. Which of the following is/are not considered as variable expenses?

(a) equipment rental
(b) operating expenses
(c) office supplies
(d) small tools

7. Fixed overhead cannot be controlled directly by management.

(a) true   (b) false

8. Which of the following is/are not considered as fixed expenses?

(a) telephone
(b) printing
(c) depreciation
(d) collection expenses

9. Use Form 508 to deposit Federal Unemployment Taxes.

(a) true   (b) false

10. Current assets are expected to flow into cash within _____.

(a) thirty days   (b) sixty days   (c) six months   (d) one year

11. All long-term assets are depreciated.

(a) true   (b) false

12. A good cash budget can accomplish which of the following?

I.   takes advantage of discount terms
II.   times operations for seasonal business decreases
III. prepares for tax liabilities
IV. helps you qualify for needed loans

(a) I, II, III & IV   (b) I, IV   (c) II   (d) III

13. The most common modern bookkeeping method is called the ___ bookkeeping.

(a) cash method   (b) single entry   (c) double entry   (d) triple entry

14. You have an asset worth $10,000.00 with an estimated useful life of eight years and a salvage value of $2,000. What is the straight-line depreciation of this asset?

(a) $1,250   (b) $1,500   (c) $1,000   (d) $2,000

15. Form 941 is used once each year to report and pay Federal Unemployment Taxes.

(a) true   (b) false

16. Which of the following are balance sheet categories?

I. Land   II. Small Tools   III. Building   IV. Trucks

(a) I only   (b) II & IV   (c) I & III   (d) I, II, III & IV

17. An accurate financial statement requires reliable information, prepared consistently from month to month. Under the accrual method of accounting, this means that you must make adjustments to you general ledger balance for accounts payable.

(a) true   (b) false

18. The books are closed (final adjustments are made to update all accounts and then recorded in the general ledger) at the end of each _____.

(a) day   (b) week   (c) month   (d) year

19. A cash budget simply budgets a certain amount of cash for a specific future use.

(a) true   (b) false

20. Depreciation allows businesses to "recover" the cost of buildings and equipment over the useful life of that property.

(a) true   (b) false

21. The Schedule of Completion is the framework of your estimate.

(a) true   (b) false

22. Materials and subcontract payments are posted directly to the job-cost ledger along with payroll and expenses.

(a) true   (b) false

23. The Source and Application of Funds form is similar to that of a standard financial statement that may be included in a package of company reports.

(a) true   (b) false

24. The "net income to sales ratio" shows the margin of profit.

(a) true   (b) false

25. The quick-assets ratio and the "acid test" are one and the same.

(a) true   (b) false

26. Which of the following types of expenses are commonly accounted for as prepaid assets?

I.   printing expenses
II.   insurance
III. office supplies
IV.   interest

(a) II & IV   (b) I & III   (c) III   (d) I, II, III & IV

27. The balance sheet will always be in-balance because Total Assets = Total Liabilities + Net Worth.

(a) true   (b) false

28. The bottom line of the cash-flow statement shows either an increase or a decrease in funds.

(a) true   (b) false

29. On the Source and Application of Funds statement, fixed assets sold for cash are reflected in net-income from operations.

(a) true   (b) false

30. The General Ledger should be as detailed as possible.

(a) true   (b) false

31. The relationship between liabilities, assets, and net worth is shown in this formula as: Liabilities less Assets equals Net Worth.

(a) true   (b) false

32. The Balance Sheet is a summary of the existing conditions of the business.

(a) true   (b) false

MECHANICS LIEN LAW

1. For perfecting her or his lien under Part I, every lienor, including laborers and persons in privity, shall record a claim of lien which shall include ____.

(a) the name of the owner
(b) a description of the real property sufficient for identification
(c) the address where notices under this Part I may be served on the lienor
(d) all of the above

2. The right of redemption upon all sales under part I of this chapter shall exist in favor of the person whose interest is sold and may be exercised in the same manner as is or may be provided for redemption of real property from sales under mortgages.

(a) true   (b) false

3. The lienor, upon receiving a summons from the clerk, has ____ days to show cause why his lien should not be enforced by action.

(a) 7   (b) 10   (c) 20   (d) 60

4. No lien shall continue for a longer period than ____ after the claim of lien has been recorded.

(a) 1 year   (b) 3 years   (c) 5 years   (d) 7 years

5. Under direct contract, liens shall be paid in the following order ____.

(a) persons other than the contractor, contractor, laborers
(b) contractors, laborers, persons other than the contractor
(c) laborers, contractors, persons other than the contractor
(d) laborers, persons other than the contractor, contractor

6. A contract may be written or oral.

(a) true   (b) false

7. Within ____ days after beginning to furnish labor, materials, or supplies, a lienor who is not in privity with the contractor, except a laborer, shall serve the contractor with notice in writing that the lienor will look to the contractor's bond for protection on the work.

(a) 10   (b) 30   (c) 45   (d) 90

8. A lienor is required to serve a written notice of nonpayment to the contractor and the surety not later than ____ days after the final furnishing of labor, services, or materials by the lienor.

(a) 10   (b) 30   (c) 45   (d) 90

9. The contractor shall furnish a true copy of the bond at the cost of reproduction to any lienor demanding it.

(a) true   (b) false

10. A lien, except that of a laborer, may be assigned by the lienor at any time before its discharge.

(a) true   (b) false

11. When any person applies for a building permit, the issuing authority shall print on the face of each permit:" Warning to owner: Your failure to record a notice of commencement may result in your paying ____ for improvements to your property.

(a) one and one-half times   (b) twice   (c) three times   (d) an unlimited amount

12. "Lienor" includes which of the following?

(a) a laborer
(b) a material man who contracts with a sub-subcontractor
(c) a sub-subcontractor
(d) all of the above

13. "Real property" means the land that is improved and the improvements thereon, excluding fixtures.

(a) true   (b) false

14. The person delivering materials that have been partly paid for may repossess them on refunding no part of the purchase price.

(a) true   (b) false

15. Any person who shall willfully furnish to another person, an affidavit containing a false statement in connection with the improvement of real property, may be guilty of ____.

(a) felony   (b) larceny   (c) embezzlement   (d) fraud

16. Any person may waive his lien at any time, either before or after furnishing services or materials.

(a) true   (b) false

17. The acceptance by the lienor of an unsecured note for any part of the amount of his demand shall not constitute a waiver of his lien.

(a) true   (b) false

18. Before paying any money directly to any lienor except the contractor or any laborer, the owner shall give the contractor at least ____ days written notice of his intention and the amount he proposes to pay each lienor.

(a) 7   (b) 10   (c) 14   (d) 30

19. When materials have been furnished and paid for by the owner, to improve real property, such materials shall not be subject to attachment.

(a) true   (b) false

20. Any lien claimed under Part I may be transferred, by any person having an interest in the real property upon which the lien is imposed, from such real property to other security by ____.

I.   filing in the clerk's office a bond executed as surety by a surety insurer licensed to do business
II. depositing in the clerk's office a sum of money
III. selling the lien for the total amount owed

(a) I only   (b) I and II   (c) I and III   (d) I, II and III

BUSINESS

LAW EXAM

FINAL EXAM   **50 QUESTIONS**

TIME LIMIT   **2 1/2 HOURS**

50 QUESTIONS   **TIME LIMIT 2.5 HOURS**

1. According to the Florida Unemployment Compensation Law, a new business is required to report its initial employment ____.

(a) **within one year**
(b) **within one month in which employment begins**
(c) **within six months in which employment begins**
(d) **within the month following the calendar quarter in which employment begins**

2. An application for an employer identification number is submitted by the employer on Form ____.

(a) SS-8   (b) SS-4   (c) CT-1   (d) 941

3. Which of the following is exempt from the Contractors Licensing Law?

(a) **Public utilities, on construction, maintenance, and development work performed by their forces and incidental to their business**
(b) **subordinates of any person engaged in contracting who is certified to engage in contracting if the employees do not hold themselves out for hire**
(c) **an officer appointed by the court when he is acting within the scope of his office as defined by law**
(d) **all of the above**

4. The minimum amount of property damage insurance required as a prerequisite to the issuance of a license is ____.

(a) $300,000   (b) $125,000   (c) $500,000   (d) none of these

5. No permit of any class may be issued to a person for the first time by the State Fire Marshal until the applicant has ____.

(a) **submitted a nonrefundable filing fee of $50**
(b) **successfully completed a training course offered by the State Fire College**
(c) **passed a written and practical exam with a grade of at least 75%**
(d) **all of the above**

6. It is not necessary for the General Ledger to be detailed.

(a) true   (b) false

7. According to the Florida Mechanics' Lien Law, when the final payment under a direct contract becomes due the contractor, said contractor shall execute an affidavit and deliver it to the owner at least _____ days before instituting an action to enforce his lien.

(a) 5   (b) 14   (c) 30   (d) 60

8. The 3 consecutive months ending March 31, June 30, September 30 and December 31 of any year are known as a calendar quarter.

(a) true   (b) false

9. A new employer has paid $8000 to an employee during a calendar year. According to Florida Unemployment Compensation what would the Florida unemployment tax be?

(a) $216   (b) $189   (c) $162   (d) $496

10. What is the social security tax contribution required by an employer if the employee is paid $475 per week?

(a) $27.12   (b) $29.45   (c) $36.57   (d) $21.72

11. All persons contracting in the state shall be registered with the Department of Professional Regulation unless they are certified.

(a) true   (b) false

12. To satisfy the continuing education requirement, the licensee must submit a notarized statement affirming the following:

(a) location and date of the course
(b) the instructors credentials
(c) benefit received from the course
(d) all of the above

13. The State Fire Marshal and his agents shall conduct performance tests on all components of any electronic fire warning and smoke detection system in any state-owned or state-leased space on a recurring basis.

(a) true   (b) false

14. You receive a $6000 payment which represents one-half of the total contract price. You know that the job is only 40% complete. What is your balance, unearned income?

(a) $2,400   (b) $4,800   (c) $6,000   (d) $1,200

15. According to the Florida Mechanics' Lien Law, a _____ may not waive his lien at any time, either before or after furnishing services or materials.

(a) subcontractor   (b) sub-subcontractor   (c) materialman   (d) laborer

16. According to the Florida Unemployment Compensation, the maximum employer's tax rate is _____.

(a) 2.7%   (b) 5.4%   (c) 1.2%   (d) 5.71%

17. The Florida Unemployment Compensation Law requires that the employee must maintain true and accurate work records for a period of _____ calendar years.

(a) 3   (b) 5   (c) 7   (d) 10

18. According to the Florida Workers' Compensation law, an employee was earning $650 per week when killed on the job. What is the maximum death benefit available to the spouse if there are no children?

(a) $200   (b) $325   (c) $487.50   (d) $650

19. An employee is married, claims two deductions and is paid $360 per week. What is his take home pay per week?

(a) $325.46   (b) $325   (c) $333   (d) $297.96

20. The Electrical Contractors' Licensing Board may impose which of the following penalties?

(a) deny an application for licensure
(b) revoke or suspend a license
(c) impose a fine not to exceed $5000 per offense
(d) all of the above

21. It shall constitute a misdemeanor of the second degree to intentionally obliterate the serial number on a fire extinguisher for purposes of falsifying service records.

(a) true   (b) false

22. Figure the straight-line depreciation of an asset worth $8,000 with an estimated useful life of ten years and a salvage value of $1,000.

(a) $800   (b) $700   (c) $1,000   (d) $1,400

23. In any action brought to enforce a lien, each party involved is responsible for their own attorney's fee.

(a) true   (b) false

24. The weekly unemployment benefit amount is 1/26th of the high quarter wages, and the maximum amount is $275.

(a) true   (b) false

25. According to workers' compensation, once an employee has reached the date of maximum medical improvement, impairment benefits are due and payable within ____ days after the carrier has knowledge of the impairment.

(a) 7   (b) 10   (c) 14   (d) 21

26. An employer who fails, without reasonable cause, to make his Federal income tax deposits when due will be assessed a penalty of ____ after 16 days late.

(a) 5%   (b) 10%   (c) 20%   (d) 25%

27. It shall constitute a misdemeanor of the second degree to intentionally recharge or repair a fire extinguisher or system improperly.

(a) true   (b) false

28. You can defer tax on income by placing up to $4000 per year in an Individual Retirement Account.

(a) true   (b) false

29. According to the Florida Mechanics' Lien Law, no lien shall continue for more than ____ after the claim of lien has been recorded.

(a) 1 year   (b) 7 years   (c) 10 years   (d) 2 years

30. Under the Florida Unemployment Compensation Law, commissions and bonuses are not considered as part of "wages".

(a) true   (b) false

31. Improperly charging workers' compensation insurers may constitite grounds for the Division of Workers' Compensation to impose a fine not to exceed ____.

(a) $2500   (b) $5000   (c) $7500   (d) $10,000

32. An employee is single, claims one withholding allowance, works 40 hours per week and is paid $11.50 per hour. After the FUTA tax liability is met, what is his take home pay?

(a) $425.45   (b) $379.81   (c) $364.73   (d) $391

33. It shall constitute a misdemeanor of the first degree to intentionally use the permit of another person.

(a) true   (b) false

34. When using double entry bookkeeping, two entries provide control throughout the bookkeeping process. A debit is an entry made to the right side, and a credit is an entry made on the left side.

(a) true   (b) false

35. "Lienor giving notice" means any lienor, except a contractor, who has duly and timely served a notice to the owner.

(a) true   (b) false

36. According to the Florida Workers' Compensation Law, no compensation shall be payable if the injury was occasioned primarily by the intoxication of the employee.

(a) true   (b) false

37. According to the Florida Unemployment Compensation Law, the weekly benefit amount to which a claimant is entitled is _____ of the high quarter wage, but not to exceed $275.

(a) 1/20th   (b) 1/26th   (c) 1/33   (d) none of these

38. If an employee who is permanently and totally disabled, and has no dependents, becomes an inmate of a public institution, said employee shall have _____.

(a) the compensation reduced to one-half
(b) the compensation reduced to one-fourth
(c) no change in the amount of compensation
(d) the compensation terminated

39. Application for a social security card may be aquired at any SSA office by completing Form _____.

(a) SS-1   (b) SS-3   (c) SS-5   (d) none of these

40. Any person initially employed as a firefighter must _____.

(a) be a high school graduate or the equivalent
(b) have his fingerprints on file with the division
(c) have good moral character
(d) all of the above

41. There are two principal methods of preparing a cash budget: the Cash-Movement method and the Source & Application of Funds method.

(a) true   (b) false

42. A lienor shall be required to record _____ covering his entire demand against the real property when the amount demanded is for labor or services or material furnished for more than one improvement under the same direct contract.

(a) one claim of lien per improvement
(b) one claim of lien
(c) one claim of lien per improvement but no more than a total of three
(d) none of the above

43. According to the Florida Unemployment Compensation Law, the employer is required to display the poster "To employees" UCT-83, in a place where all employees can see it.

(a) true   (b) false

44. The Worker's'Compensation Law states: An employer is to file a report of injury with the Division of Workers' Compensation within _____ after learning of an employee's injury.

(a) 24 hours   (b) 48 hours   (c) 7 days   (d) 10 working days

45. Certificates issued by the State Fire Marshal shall expire annually at midnight on July 30.

(a) true   (b) false

46. A builders' variable overhead expenses includes: printing, operating supplies, equipment rental and small tools; to name a few.

(a) true   (b) false

47. According to the Florida Mechanics' Lien Law, the person delivering materials that have been partly paid for may repossess them by refunding the part of the purchase price which has been paid.

(a) true   (b) false

48. Payments received under a workmen's compensation law are not subject to social security taxes.

(a) true   (b) false

49. Which of the following reduces your tax rate?

I.   Timing asset sales to delay recognition of a gain
II. Making contributions
III. Timing asset purchases to minimize the depreciation and expensing provisions under the law.
IV. Periodic reviews with your accountant or tax-advisor.

(a) I & III   (b) I, II & IV   (c) III & IV   (d) All of the above

50. Generally, all employers who are subject to income tax withholding or social security taxes must file Form _____ quarterly.

(a) 941   (b) 1-9   (c) 521   (d) 8109

ANSWERS

N.E.C. EXAM ANSWERS

1. **(c)** 90.1 A
2. **(d)** 90.2
3. **(c)** 90.4
4. **(a)** 110.2
5. **(c)** 110.4
6. **(c)** 110.5
7. **(b)** 110.8
8. **(c)** 110.11
9. **(c)** 110.12
10. **(c)** 110.12 A
11. **(b)** 110.26 A 2
12. **(b)** 240.8
13. **(b)** 240.10
14. **(b)** Art. 100, Def.
15. **(a)** 240.15 A
16. **(b)** 240.21
17. **(c)** 240.24 D
18. **(a)** 312.2
19. **(c)** 240.41 A
20. **(c)** 250.4 A 2
21. **(d)** 250.162A
22. **(d)** 250.20A 1,2,3
23. **(a)** 250.20 D
24. **(d)** 250.30 (1) ex. #3
25. **(c)** 250.110 (1)

26. **(c)** 250.4 A 5
27. **(d)** 250.53 G
28. **(a)** 250.60 I.N. #2
29. **(d)** 250.64 B
30. **(d)** 250.172 ex.
31. **(a)** 300.3 C 1
32. **(a)** 300.4 A 1
33. **(b)** 300.14
34. **(c)** 300.17
35. **(a)** 300.21
36. **(b)** 300.22 C 3
37. **(d)** 720.2, 720.4
38. **(c)** 725.139 D 1
39. **(c)** 725.31 A
40. **(d)** 725.41 A
41. **(d)** 725.51 A
42. **(c)** 450.11, 725.41 A 1
43. **(b)** 725.43
44. **(b)** 725.136 A
45. **(c)** 250.162 A ex. 3
46. **(d)** 760.41,43,48 A
47. **(a)** 760.53 A 1
48. **(d)** 760.49 A
49. **(b)** 760.179 B
50. **(a)** 770.2 Def.

OHMS LAW EXAM

1. **(d)** $W = E^2/R = \dfrac{10 \times 10}{5} = \dfrac{100}{5} = \mathbf{20}$

2. **(b)** all in parallel
3. **(d)** Conductance
4. **(d)** 1000 amp turns
5. **(b)** watt
6. **(c)** voltage drop
7. **(c)** current
8. **(a)** $9\Omega/3 = 3$
9. **(b)** shorted
10. **(d)** the relationship between voltage, current and resistance
11. **(b)** 14.4Ω resistor $\quad R = E^2/W = \dfrac{120 \times 120}{1000} = 14.4\Omega$

12. **(b)** voltage
13. **(a)** impedance
14. **(a)** voltage
15. **(b)** decrease
16. **(d)** 1000 watts $\quad W = I^2R = 10 \times 10 \times 10 = 1000$
17. **(b)** 2.5Ω $\quad 10\Omega/4 = 2.5\Omega$ total
18. **(c)** a 10Ω resistor
19. **(d)** rectifiers change DC to AC
20. **(a)** 1 amp $\quad I = E/R = 12\Omega/12v = 1$ amp
21. **(a)** the sum of the individual resistance values
22. **(d)** 1227 watt $\quad R = E^2/W = \dfrac{230 \times 230}{1500} = 35.266666\Omega \quad W = E^2/R = \dfrac{208 \times 208}{35.266666} = 1226.7\Omega$

23. **(c)** 220 watt $\quad W = E \times I = 110 \times 2 = 220$
24. **(c)** 6000 watts $\quad W = I^2R = 20 \times 20 \times 15 = 6000$
25. **(c)** 6 volts

1. **(c)** $7.77\Omega \times .040' = 0.3108\Omega$

2. **(b)** Exact K = $\dfrac{5.08\Omega \times 2580cm}{1000} = 13.1064$ D = $\dfrac{2580cm \times 0.36\ VD\ per}{2 \times 13.1064 \times 0.75a} = 47.2$ feet

3. **(c)** CM = $\dfrac{2 \times \mathbf{12.9} \times 75' \times 1.5a}{0.72\ VD\ per} = 4031$ CM required = Table 8 = #14

4. **(b)** Table 8 = #16 = 4.99Ω per M/FT/ 1000' = $.00499\Omega$ per foot $\dfrac{.43\Omega}{.00499\Omega} = 86.1$ feet

5. **(b)** **VD = I x R**   I = E/R = 6v/50Ω = .12 amp   I = .12 amp
   Table 8 = #14 = 3.07Ω per M/FT x .080' = $.2456\Omega$ R = $.2456\Omega$
   VD = .12a x $.2456\Omega$ = .029472 volt dropped

6. **(c)** Table 8 = #16 = 4.89Ω per M/FT x .085' = $\dfrac{.41565\Omega}{2\ (parallel)} = 0.207825\Omega$

7. **(b)** Exact K = $\dfrac{8.08\Omega \times 1620cm}{1000'} = 13.0896$ I = $\dfrac{1620cm \times 0.36\ VD\ per}{2 \times 13.0896 \times 65'} = 0.34$ amp

8. **(b)** CM = $\dfrac{2 \times \mathbf{12.9} \times 50' \times .25a}{.18\ VD\ per} = 1791$cm required   Table 8 = #16

9. **(c)** Table 8 = #18 = 7.95Ω per M/FT/ 1000' = $.00795\Omega$ per foot
   $\dfrac{1.05\Omega}{.00795\Omega}$ = $\dfrac{132\ feet\ of\ wire}{2}$ = 66 feet distance

10. **(b)** VD = I x R   I = .36 amp
    Table 8 = #14 = 3.14Ω per M/FT x .112' = $.35168\Omega$
    VD = .36a x $.35168\Omega$ = .1266048 volt dropped

1. **(a)** Table 4 = .533

2. **(d)** Table 4 = 1.496 x 60% = .897

3. **(b)** Table 5 =   14 - #16 TF   = .0109 x 14   = .1526
                   16 - #16 TFN   = .0072 x 16   = .1152
                   12 - #14 THHN   = .0097 x 12   = .1164
                    1 - #14 bare solid   = .003 (Table 8)
                                            .3872 sq.in. = Table 4 = 1 1/4" @ 40% fill

4. **(b)** Table C1

5. **(c)** Chapter 9 Note 4

6. **(d)** Table 5 = .0075 sq.in.

1. **(c)** 14.2.2.1
2. **(b)** 17.11.4
3. **(d)** 10.17.1.15
4. **(d)** 29.5.1.1
5. **(d)** 17.6.2.2.1.1
6. **(a)** 10.6.2
7. **(a)** 29.8.3.4
8. **(c)** 29.6.3 (2)
9. **(d)** T.14.4.2.2
10. **(d)** T. A.18.4.3
11. **(c)** 17.14.6
12. **(c)** 17.7.3.2.1
13. **(d)** 29.5.1.1
14. **(b)** 29.6.6(1)
15. **(c)** 3.3.31.4
16. **(b)** 3.3.31.3
17. **(a)** 26.4.4.6.2
18. **(d)** 23.8.5.4.1
19. **(c)** 10.11.2
20. **(b)** 10.5.5.1(1)
21. **(c)** 17.14.4
22. **(d)** 10.14.2.3
23. **(b)** 3.3.95.1
24. **(c)** 10.11.5.2 & 3
25. **(c)** 10.17.2.1.1 & 3

26. **(a)** 12.2.4.4
27. **(d)** 18.3.3.1
28. **(d)** 10.17.1.1
29. **(a)** 17.16.2.2.1
30. **(a)** 14.4.7.1
31. **(b)** 17.14.6
         17.14.8
32. **(d)** 10.5.7.2
33. **(a)** 10.7.3
34. **(a)** 10.11.5.3
35. **(c)** 23.8.5.3.1
36. **(c)** 10.17.1.1
37. **(d)** 27.6.3.2.3.1
38. **(a)** 14.6.2.1
39. **(d)** 3.3.8.4
40. **(c)** 3.3.8.3
41. **(b)** 72
42. **(a)** 17.6.2.3
43. **(a)** 10.18.3.1
44. **(d)** 29.8.2.2 (2)
45. **(d)** 23.8.5.11.1
46. **(d)** 17.6.3.1.2
47. **(c)** 27.6.3.2.2.1(2)E
48. **(a)** 26.4.5.1.1
49. **(d)** 10.14.1
50. **(a)** 3.3.266

51. **(a)** 10.7.5
52. **(b)** 3.3.199.1
53. **(d)** 27.5.2.6.4
54. **(d)** 27.6.3.2.2.1(2)D
55. **(b)** 10.14.2.3
56. **(c)** 26.6.3.2.3.3(A)
57. **(b)** 26.4.5.6.2
58. **(a)** 3.3.240.7
59. **(d)** 10.5.10.6
60. **(c)** 3.3.240.2
61. **(d)** 26.5.3.1.2 & 3
62. **(d)** 10.5.7.2
63. **(a)** 17.6.3.6
64. **(a)** 23.8.5.5.2
65. **(a)** 26.4.4.2.1.3
66. **(d)** 27.6.2.1.10
67. **(b)** 10.16.6.1
68. **(b)** 3.3.240.1
69. **(a)** 10.3.1
70. **(d)** 23.8.1.3.1.1(1)
71. **(d)** 10.5.5.2.2 & 3
72. **(a)** 7.16.1.2
73. **(c)** 23.15.4
74. **(a)** 26.4.4.4(2)
75. **(b)** 23.16.4

76. **(a)** 3.3.66
77. **(d)** 12.2.4.4 ex
78. **(a)** 17.16.4.1
79. **(b)** 17.6.3.1.3.2
80. **(c)** 17.7.5.5.7
81. **(a)** 14.3.4
82. **(a)** 27.6.3.2.3.7
83. **(b)** 3.3.103
84. **(a)** 17.6.3.4.2.1
85. **(b)** 3.3.59.21
86. **(b)** 14.6.1.3
87. **(c)** 17.7.5.6.6.1
88. **(c)** 3.3.59.7
89. **(a)** 17.7.1.8
90. **(b)** 3.3.59.18
91. **(b)** 17.7.3.2.3.1
92. **(d)** 27.7.1.2.6
93. **(d)** 17.7.5.5.2
94. **(a)** 17.5.3.1.5
95. **(a)** 3.3.59.5
96. **(d)** 17.7.3.1.2
97. **(b)** 3.3.33.4
98. **(c)** 14.4.5.3.6
99. **(b)** 14.4.5.2
100. **(d)** 17.7.1.9

1. **(c)** 17.7.3.2.4.6
2. **(d)** 14.2.4
3. **(b)** 29.8.3.2
4. **(c)** 17.12.2
5. **(d)** 17.12.3
6. **(a)** 3.3.59.8
7. **(a)** 14.4.5.3.7
8. **(a)** 26.4.4.6.2
9. **(b)** 26.5.3.1.1
10. **(a)** 27.6.3.2.2.1 (2) a
11. **(b)** 27.5.5.3.7.2
12. **(c)** 3.3.3
13. **(a)** 3.3.95.2
14. **(a)** 3.3.59.8
15. **(d)** Table 17.6.2.1
16. **(b)** 3.3.224
17. **(c)** 10.5.9.2
18. **(d)** 26.5.5.2
19. **(a)** 3.3.199.1.1
20. **(b)** 17.16.4.2
21. **(d)** 17.14.8
22. **(a)** 17.16.3.2
23. **(d)** 3.3.29
24. **(a)** 3.3.122.3
25. **(a)** 10.18.3.2
26. **(a)** 3.3.31.1
27. **(c)** 3.3.54
28. **(d)** 14.6.1.3
29. **(d)** 17.7.3.2.1
30. **(d)** 17.7.5.4.1
31. **(d)** 17.7.3.2.1
32. **(a)** 23.15.4 & 5
33. **(d)** 10.10.3
34. **(b)** A.3.3.252.2
35. **(a)** 17.7.3.2.3.5
36. **(c)** 26.4.3.4.3
37. **(b)** Table 14.4.5 (5)(a)(3)
38. **(a)** 29.6.2 (1)
39. **(c)** 3.3.31.1
40. **(b)** 10.9.3
41. **(c)** 27.6.3.2.2.1 (2) f
42. **(c)** 3.3.182
43. **(a)** 26.6.3.2.1.5 (5)
44. **(c)** 10.5.9.4.2
45. **(a)** 3.3.127.1.1
46. **(a)** 3.3.59.8
47. **(d)** A.3.3.59.18 (3)
48. **(b)** 17.14.4
49. **(a)** 3.3.59.10
50. **(a)** 17.4.4

ANSWERS 51 - 100 CONTINUED ON THE NEXT PAGE

51.	**(a)**	17.4.7	76.	**(d)**	21.3.3 & 4
52.	**(a)**	3.3.282	77.	**(b)**	10.6.6
53.	**(d)**	10.5.6.3.1 (3)	78.	**(d)**	17.16.3.3
54.	**(a)**	14.4.1.2.2	79.	**(b)**	3.3.224
55.	**(d)**	17.11.3	80.	**(c)**	17.6.3.4.2.1
56.	**(a)**	17.14.1	81.	**(b)**	3.3.33.3
57.	**(d)**	17.6.3.6	82.	**(c)**	10.18.3.1
58.	**(d)**	10.3.1	83.	**(c)**	3.3.129
59.	**(d)**	26.4.4.1.3	84.	**(c)**	26.3.5.2.3
60.	**(b)**	14.2.2.1	85.	**(d)**	18.3.3.1
61.	**(c)**	17.14.7	86.	**(d)**	Table 14.4.5 (15)(f)
62.	**(c)**	23.18.2 (4)	87.	**(b)**	17.14.8
63.	**(d)**	3.3.59.19	88.	**(d)**	Table 18.5.4.6.2
64.	**(a)**	17.7.3.4	89.	**(b)**	3.3.266
65.	**(a)**	3.3.240.6	90.	**(d)**	3.3.263
66.	**(d)**	10.5.7.2	91.	**(b)**	23.16.5
67.	**(a)**	23.8.5.8.2	92.	**(c)**	A.3.3.59.7
68.	**(b)**	17.14.4	93.	**(a)**	17.14.1 & 2
69.	**(b)**	12.2.4.4	94.	**(c)**	Table 14.4.2.2 (14 g)
70.	**(d)**	3.3.40	95.	**(a)**	3.3.173
71.	**(a)**	3.3.3	96.	**(a)**	3.3.177.1
72.	**(a)**	23.8.5.5.1	97.	**(d)**	3.3.252
73.	**(a)**	17.14	98.	**(a)**	29.6.6 (1) & (5)
74.	**(a)**	14.2.2.3	99.	**(b)**	10.3.1
75.	**(b)**	10.9.3	100.	**(a)**	A.3.2.5

1. **(c)** 8.3.4
2. **(a)** 8.3.2
3. **(d)** 8.2.1
4. **(c)** 8.1.3
5. **(d)** 10.4.2 (1)
6. **(b)** 5.4.2
7. **(d)** 10.1.1
8. **(d)** 10.4.8
9. **(d)** 10.4.4 (2)
10. **(c)** 10.4.1
11. **(d)** 10.1.2
12. **(c)** 9.1 (1)
13. **(b)** 11.3
14. **(d)** 10.4.6
15. **(c)** 10.4.11

1. **(d)** 4.1.2.2
2. **(a)** 4.7.4.1
3. **(b)** 4.7.3.2
4. **(c)** 4.6.2.1
5. **(d)** 4.3.2
6. **(b)** 4.1.1.1 1
7. **(a)** 3.3.1
8. **(a)** 4.13.5.2
9. **(b)** 4.13.2.3 1
10. **(a)** A.4.13.2
11. **(c)** 4.9.11.2
12. **(c)** 4.13.2.1
13. **(d)** 4.9.10.1
14. **(a)** 4.9.8.1
15. **(b)** 4.9.1
16. **(c)** 10.3.2.3
17. **(d)** B.5
18. **(c)** 4.20.1.1
19. **(d)** 4.20.3
20. **(a)** 4.21.3.2
21. **(a)** 4.16.1
22. **(d)** 4.15.3.2
23. **(a)** 9.2.6
24. **(a)** 8.5.8
25. **(d)** 4.16.4.1

1. **(d)** 1.2
2. **(a)** 3.3.214
3. **(c)** 4.6.10.1
4. **(b)** 3.3.27
5. **(b)** 3.3.47
6. **(a)** 3.3.22
7. **(d)** 7.2.4.3.1
8. **(b)** 7.1.7.1
9. **(c)** Table 7.2.2.2.1 (b)
10. **(d)** 7.2.1.2.3.2 (2)
11. **(b)** 7.2.1.3.1
12. **(c)** 7.2.1.2.3.2
13. **(a)** 7.2.1.7.1 (3)
14. **(d)** 7.1.9
15. **(d)** 7.2.1.10.2 (1) (2)
16. **(a)** 7.2.1.11.1.2(3)
17. **(d)** Table 7.2.2.2.1.1 (b)
18. **(b)** 7.2.2.2.3.3 (1), (5), 7.2.2.2.3.4
19. **(b)** 7.1.8
20. **(a)** 7.6.1 (1)
21. **(d)** 7.6.4
22. **(b)** 7.5.4.1
23. **(a)** 7.8.2.1
24. **(c)** 7.9.1.3
25. **(a)** 7.9.2.3 (1)(2)

26. **(c)** 7.8.2.2
27. **(b)** 7.9.2.1
28. **(b)** 43.5.2.3
29. **(a)** 7.10.6.3
30. **(d)** 7.10.1.6
31. **(c)** 7.10.1.5.2
32. **(a)** 7.11.1
33. **(b)** 8.3.3.5
34. **(c)** 8.3.5.4 (1)
35. **(a)** 9.6.2.3 (2)
36. **(c)** 9.6.2.8
37. **(a)** 9.6.7.3
38. **(d)** 9.6.7.4
39. **(c)** 12.7.9.1.1
40. **(d)** 12.1.7.2 (3)
41. **(a)** Table 7.3.1.2 concentrated use
42. **(d)** 12.2.2.2.3
43. **(c)** 12.2.3.6.6
44. **(d)** 12.2.6.2
45. **(a)** 14.2.5.5
46. **(d)** 15.2.6.3
47. **(d)** 22.2.11.12.1
48. **(b)** 30.2.2.1.2
49. **(d)** 42.2.9, 42.2.8.2
50. **(c)** 14.7.2.3 (1)

1.	**(d)**	681	5.1.1
2.	**(d)**	681	1.2
3.	**(c)**	365	Table 36.3
4.	**(d)**	681	6.2.4
5.	**(a)**	681	10.1.3
6.	**(d)**	681	2.2.3
7.	**(b)**	365	74.10
8.	**(a)**	681	15.1.2
9.	**(c)**	681	22.2.3
10.	**(d)**	365	84.2
11.	**(d)**	365	1.3
12.	**(a)**	365	8.2
13.	**(b)**	365	65.1
14.	**(b)**	365	15.2
15.	**(c)**	681	4.3.2.3
16.	**(b)**	681	6.2.1
17.	**(a)**	681	10.2.1
18.	**(c)**	365	48.1.1
19.	**(a)**	365	64.10
20.	**(d)**	365	Table 86.1
21.	**(d)**	365	87.5
22.	**(d)**	681	3.42
23.	**(b)**	681	16.1.4
24.	**(b)**	365	table 7.1
25.	**(d)**	681	10.4.7
26.	**(c)**	681	11.3.3
27.	**(c)**	681	22.2.2
28.	**(a)**	365	Table 113.1
29.	**(c)**	681	3.40
30.	**(a)**	681	7-3
31.	**(d)**	365	44.1
32.	**(c)**	365	48.2.1
33.	**(b)**	681	6.5.1
34.	**(c)**	365	55.2
35.	**(c)**	681	8.4
36.	**(d)**	365	9.1
37.	**(b)**	365	12.2.2.5
38.	**(d)**	681	6.5.3
39.	**(a)**	365	54.4
40.	**(d)**	365	12.2.2.3
41.	**(c)**	365	11.3
42.	**(c)**	365	12.2.3.1 (d)
43.	**(d)**	365	7.7.1
44.	**(c)**	365	3.4 (b)
45.	**(a)**	681	22.1.3
46.	**(d)**	681	16.1.1
47.	**(a)**	681	19.8 b
48.	**(b)**	681	7.1
49.	**(d)**	681	9.2
50.	**(d)**	681	4.1.2.1, 4.1.3.1, 4.1.4.1
51.	**(d)**	365	7.3.5
52.	**(a)**	365	17.3
53.	**(b)**	681	Table 5.1
54.	**(b)**	681	6.7.1
55.	**(a)**	365	11.3
56.	**(d)**	365	5.2.2
57.	**(d)**	365	6.3 & 6.4 (a) (b) (c)
58.	**(b)**	365	8.3
59.	**(c)**	681	6.4.1
60.	**(c)**	681	11.6.2
61.	**(c)**	681	7.3a
62.	**(a)**	681	24.2
63.	**(a)**	681	5.2.1
64.	**(b)**	681	22.1.6
65.	**(c)**	365	12.2.2.2
66.	**(c)**	365	12.2.3.2 b
67.	**(b)**	365	12.3.1
68.	**(c)**	681	23.5.2
69.	**(b)**	681	5.5.1
70.	**(a)**	681	21.2.2
71.	**(c)**	365	74.14
72.	**(c)**	681	5.1.1
73.	**(c)**	365	78.1
74.	**(b)**	681	11.1.4
75.	**(c)**	681	6.2.1
76.	**(d)**	365	84.2 (a) & 85
77.	**(c)**	365	12.2.1.3
78.	**(d)**	681	16.3.4
79.	**(c)**	365	79.2
80.	**(a)**	681	20.2 (b)

OSHA EXAM

1. **(b)** 404 b1ii
2. **(c)** 950 c2i Table V-1
3. **(b)** 800-S-3
4. **(a)** 405 a 2 ii B
5. **(d)** 102a
6. **(b)** 107b
7. **(c)** 200c
8. **(c)** Appendix A Subpart L table
9. **(d)** 52e
10. **(c)** 51 Table D-1
11. **(b)** 104d
12. **(b)** 650b
13. **(d)** 56A Table D-3
14. **(c)** 451 g 4 vii
15. **(c)** 416 a2
16. **(c)** 956a 3i
17. **(d)** 853
18. **(a)** 803 j2
19. **(a)** 756a
20. **(d)** 350 a 11
21. **(a)** 151 d5
22. **(a)** Appendix A Subpart L (c) iii
23. **(d)** Appendix A Subpart L A(p)3
24. **(a)** 150 Table F-1
25. **(b)** 960 ff

26. **(b)** 56a Table D-3
27. **(b)** 302e
28. **(b)** 201 a4
29. **(d)** 416 e2
30. **(b)** 959 b1 ii
31. **(c)** 850 b
32. **(b)** 902 h
33. **(b)** 800 g3
34. **(c)** 550 c4
35. **(a)** Appendix A Subpart L (p)4
36. **(c)** 350a2
37. **(c)** 351 c2
38. **(d)** 300 d3
39. **(c)** 1101n 2
40. **(a)** 104 a
41. **(b)** 20 b1
42. **(a)** 651 c2
43. **(b)** 405c
44. **(b)** 150 c1 vi
45. **(b)** 56a Table D-3
46. **(c)** Appendix A Subpart L (2) e
47. **(a)** 105 d
48. **(d)** 441 a6
49. **(c)** 955 Table V-2
50. **(a)** 1053 b 19

OSHA EXAM ANSWERS CONTINUED ON THE NEXT PAGE

51. **(a)** 451 f 2
52. **(a)** 453 b 2 j
53. **(b)** 501 b 1
54. **(a)** 151 d 7
55. **(a)** 250 b1
56. **(a)** 1053 a 4 i
57. **(a)** 52 Table D-2
58. **(d)** 100 a
59. **(c)** 906 e
60. **(d)** 800 o 4 i
61. **(d)** 800 (k) 2
62. **(d)** 1052a4
63. **(d)** 352 c
64. **(b)** 150 Table F-1
65. **(c)** 1053 a 4 ii
66. **(b)** 251 c 4 iv
67. **(c)** 754 b2
68. **(b)** Appendix B Subpart P Table B-1
69. **(c)** 1501 a 15 i
70. **(b)** 150 a 3
71. **(c)** 251 a 1
72. **(c)** 105 a
73. **(c)** 104 b
74. **(a)** 350 f 3
75. **(d)** 951 a 1 iii

76. **(b)** 804 a
77. **(d)** 453b2v
78. **(c)** 451b5i
79. **(c)** Appendix A Subpart L Part 2 b Table
80. **(a)** 151 d 7
81. **(b)** 552 c 14 iii
82. **(b)** 1000
83. **(d)** 150 Table F-1
84. **(b)** 152 b 2
85. **(c)** 352 j
86. **(d)** 451c 2 ii
87. **(d)** 502b1
88. **(d)** 150 Table F-1
89. **(a)** 452 e 4
90. **(c)** 900 k 1
91. **(d)** 760 a 2
92. **(a)** 651 i 3
93. **(d)** 500 b def.
94. **(b)** 452 k 1
95. **(b)** 405 a 2 ii J
96. **(d)** 106 c
97. **(c)** 56 Table D-3
98. **(b)** 150 c 1 i
99. **(b)** Appendix A Subpart L (j)
100. **(a)** 50 d 2

FLORIDA UNEMPLOYMENT

1. **(b)** page 1
2. **(a)** page 24
3. **(b)** page 3
4. **(a)** page 22 ($9000 x 2.7% = $243.00)
5. **(d)** page 24
6. **(c)** page 24
7. **(a)** page14
8. **(b)** page 20 ($25 per month x 3 months = $75.00)
9. **(d)** page 27
10. **(b)** page 26
11. **(c)** page 5
12. **(d)** page 14
13. **(b)** page 22
14. **(b)** page 23
15. **(d)** page 29
16. **(b)** page 28
17. **(c)** page 19
18. **(b)** page 8
19. **(a)** page 12
20. **(d)** page 17

WORKERS COMPENSATION

1. **(b)** 440.02 (6)
2. **(c)** 440.185 (3)
3. **(b)** 440.09 (5)
4. **(b)** 440.02 (5)
5. **(a)** 440.12 (1)
6. **(d)** 440.16 (1) b
7. **(a)** 440.12 (2)
8. **(b)** 440.185 (1)
9. **(b)** 440.54
10. **(a)** 440.15 (4) (e)
11. **(b)** 440.185 (2)
12. **(c)** 440.02 (1)
13. **(d)** 440.185 (2)
14. **(b)** 440.20 (2) (b)
15. **(a)** 440.20 (7)
16. **(a)** 440.20 (13)
17. **(b)** 440.151 (6)
18. **(a)** 440.02 (b)
19. **(c)** 440.02 (20)
20. **(b)** 440.02 (2)

CIRCULAR E

1. **(b)** page 34
2. **(d)** page 24
3. **(b)** page 4, 15
4. **(b)** page 17
5. **(b)** page 17
6. **(a)** page 29
7. **(a)** page 8
8. **(a)** page 42
    TAX TABLES ($475 - $25 income tax - $29.45 social security - $6.89 medicare = $413.66)
9. **(a)** page 8
10. **(a)** page 23
11. **(d)** page 29
12. **(b)** page 40
    TAX TABLES ($325 - $34 income tax - $20.15 social security - $4.71 medicare = $266.14)
13. **(a)** page 5
14. **(c)** page 24
15. **(b)** page 30
16. **(c)** page 30
17. **(a)** page 14
18. **(b)** page 23
19. **(d)** page 18
20. **(a)** page 2

1. **(a)** Page 18
2. **(c)** Page 16
3. **(c)** Page 10
4. **(c)** $400/50 hrs. = $8 per hr. $8/2 = $4 x 10 hrs. = $40 + $400 = $440   Page 14
5. **(d)** Page 1
6. **(b)** $8/2 = $4 + $8 = $12.00 Page 13
7. **(c)** $600/40 hrs = $15 per hour
    $15/2 = $7.50 premimum pay.
    $7.50 + $15 = $22.50 x 8 = $180 + $600 = $780 Page 13, 14
8. **(b)** 400 boards x $1.50 = $600
    $600/50hrs = $12.00 per hr. $12.00/2 = $6.00 premimum pay,
    $6.00 x 10 hrs = $60 + $600=$660   Page 13
9. **(d)** Page 16
10. **(a)** Page 8

FLORIDA STATUTES

1. **(c)** 489.509
2. **(a)** 489.519(1)
3. **(b)** 489.519
4. **(a)** 489.507(1)
5. **(d)** 489.533(2)
6. **(a)** 489.521(1)
7. **(a)** 489.533(4)
8. **(d)** 489.507(1)
9. **(d)** 489.503(3,9,11)
10. **(d)** 489.523
11. **(d)** 489.533 (4)(p)
12. **(c)** 489.521(5)
13. **(b)** 489.507(6)
14. **(d)** 489.533(1)(f,h,i)
15. **(b)** 61 G6-4.016
16. **(a)** 61 G6-5.004(3)
17. **(a)** 61 G6-5.008 (1)h
18. **(a)** 61 G6-6.005(1)
19. **(b)** 61 G6-8.001(1)
20. **(b)** 61 G6-8.001(4)
21. **(b)** 61 G6-8.001(5)
22. **(a)** Chapter 633.061(1)(b)
23. **(a)** Chapter 633.082(1)
24. **(b)** Chapter 633.081(5)
25. **(d)** Chapter 633.35(1)
26. **(c)** Chapter 633.162(1)

1. **(c)** page 247
2. **(b)** page 24 $16,000 x 40% = $6400 $8000 - $6400= $1600
3. **(a)** page 8
4. **(b)** page 137
5. **(a)** page 142, 143
6. **(c)** page 142
7. **(b)** page 142
8. **(d)** page 142
9. **(a)** page 138
10. **(d)** page 252
11. **(b)** page 162
12. **(a)** page 173, 174
13. **(c)** page 15
14. **(c)** page 163, 164
15. **(b)** page 137, 138
16. **(d)** page 247, 248
17. **(a)** page 281, 282
18. **(d)** page 284
19. **(b)** page 173
20. **(a)** page 161
21. **(a)** page 226
22. **(b)** page 202
23. **(a)** page 176
24. **(a)** page 272
25. **(a)** page 269
26. **(d)** page 240
27. **(a)** page 248
28. **(a)** page 248
29. **(b)** page 177
30. **(b)** page 278
31. **(b)** page 273
32. **(a)** page 247

1. **(d)** 713.08
2. **(a)** 713.26
3. **(c)** 713.21(4)
4. **(a)** 713.22(1)
5. **(d)** 713.06(4)(a)
6. **(a)** 713.01(6)
7. **(c)** 713.23(1)(c)
8. **(d)** 713.23(1)(d)
9. **(a)** 713.23(1)(b)
10. **(a)** 713.19
11. **(b)** 713.135(1)(a)
12. **(d)** 713.01(18)
13. **(b)** 713.01(26)
14. **(b)** 713.15
15. **(a)** 713.35
16. **(b)** 713.20(2)
17. **(a)** 713.20(1)
18. **(b)** 713.06(6g)
19. **(a)** 713.17
20. **(b)** 713.24(1)a, b

1. **(d)** FL Unemp. Comp Page 9
2. **(b)** Circular E page 8
3. **(d)** 489.503 (2) (3) (4)
4. **(c)** 61G6-5.008 h (2)
5. **(b)** 633.061 (3) f
6. **(a)** Builder's Guide to Account. Pg. 278
7. **(a)** Mech. Lien Law 713.06 (5) (d) (1)
8. **(a)** FL Unemp. Comp. page 13 DEF.
9. **(a)** FL Unemp. Comp. page 23
($8000 x 2.7% = $216)
10. **(b)** Circular E ($475 x .062 = $29.45) Pg. 17
11. **(a)** 489.513 (1)
12. **(d)** 61G6-9.002 (c)
13. **(a)** 633.085 (2)
14. **(d)** Builder's Guide to Account. Pg. 23
15. **(d)** Mech. Lien Law 713.19
16. **(b)** FL Unemp. Comp. page 23
17. **(b)** FL Unemp. Comp. page 21
18. **(b)** FL Work. Comp. Law 440.16 (b) (1)
19. **(a)** Circular E TAX TABLE Page 42
$360 - $7 income tax = $353
$353 - $22.32 SS = $330.68
$330.68 - $5.22 Medicare = $325.46
20. **(d)** 489.533 (2) (a) (b) (c)
21. **(b)** 633.171 (2) (b)
22. **(b)** Builder's Guide to Account. Pg. 163
23. **(b)** Mech. Lien Law 713.29
24. **(a)** FL Unemp. Comp. page 26
25. **(c)** FL Work. Comp. Law 440.15 (3) a
26. **(b)** Circular E page 24
27. **(b)** 633.171(2) (c)
28. **(b)** Builder's Guide to Account. Pg. 344
29. **(a)** Mech. Lien Law 713.22 (1)
30. **(b)** FL Unemp. Comp. Page 14
31. **(b)** FL Work. Comp Law. 440.13(8)b(5)
32. **(b)** Circular E p.40 ($11.50 x 40 = $460)
$460 - $45 income tax = $415
$415 - $28.52 SS = $386.48
$386.48 - $6.67 Medicare = $379.81
33. **(a)** 633.171 (2) (d)
34. **(b)** Builder's Guide to Account. Pg. 15
35. **(a)** Mech. Lien Law 713.01(19)
36. **(a)** FL Work. Comp Law 440.09 (3)
37. **(b)** FL Unemp. Comp. page 26
38. **(d)** FL Work. Comp. 440.15 (8)
39. **(c)** Circular E page 9
40. **(d)** 633.34 (1) (3) (4)
41. **(a)** Builder's Guide to Account. Pg. 176
42. **(b)** Mech. Lien Law 713.09
43. **(a)** FL Unemp. Comp. page 33
44. **(c)** FL Work. Comp. 440.185 (2)
45. **(b)** 633.537 (1)
46. **(b)** Builder's Guide to Account. Pg.142, 143
47. **(a)** Mech. Lien Law 713.15
48. **(a)** Circular E page 35
49. **(b)** Builder's Guide to Accounting Page 344, 345
50. **(a)** Circular E page 25

READ THE BOOKS THE ELECTRICIANS READ

WORLDWIDE LEADER IN ELECTRICAL EDUCATION

1-800-642-2633
E-mail tomhenry@code-electrical.com
ON LINE SHOPPING AT
http://www.code-electrical.com

Tom Henry's Code Electrical Classes Inc.

Since 1979 we have taught electrical exam preparation classes in 21 states, 84 cities and St. Croix in the Virgin Islands.

Schedule a class in your city by calling 1-800-642-2633.

Alabama
Birmingham, Huntsville, Mobile, Montgomery

Arkansas
Little Rock

Connecticut
Hartford

Florida
Fort Myers, Fort Lauderdale, Lakeland, Tampa, St. Petersburg, Bradenton, Sarasota, Winter Haven, Jacksonville, Ocala, Leesburg, Daytona Beach, Orlando, Kissimmee, Winter Park, Haines City, Cocoa Beach, Ft. Pierce. Naples

Georgia
Atlanta, Macon, Gainesville

Hawaii
Honolulu

Indiana
Fort Wayne, Indianapolis, South Bend, Evansville, Muncie, Kokomo, Michigan City, Elkhart

Iowa
Des Moines, Cedar Rapids

Kansas
Wichita, Manhattan, Topeka, Salina, Dodge City

Kentucky
Louisville, Owensboro, Lexington

Louisiana
New Orleans, Shreveport, Baton Rouge, Covington

Michigan
Detroit, Grand Rapids

Mississippi
Jackson

Missouri
St. Louis, Kansas City, Springfield, Joplin, St. Joseph

North Carolina
Raleigh

Ohio
Columbus, Cincinnati, Akron

Oklahoma
Oklahoma City

Pennsylvania
Allentown

South Carolina
Columbia, Greenville, Spartanburg

Tennessee
Chattanooga, Memphis, Knoxville, Johnson City, Nashville, Jackson

Texas
Dallas, Lubbock, Amarillo, Wichita Falls, Waco, Odessa, Corpus Christi, Abilene, Longview, Plainview, San Angelo, Houston, San Antonio, College Station

http://www.code-electrical.com